Houghton Mifflin Harcourt.

COURSE I

mSpace Volume 2

Mindset Works® is a registered trademark of Mindset Works, Inc.

Printed in the U.S.A.

ISBN 978-0-545-84853-4

15 16 17 18 19 20 0029 25 24 23 22 21 20

4510006877

Contents Volume 2

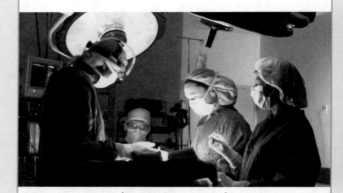

Contents

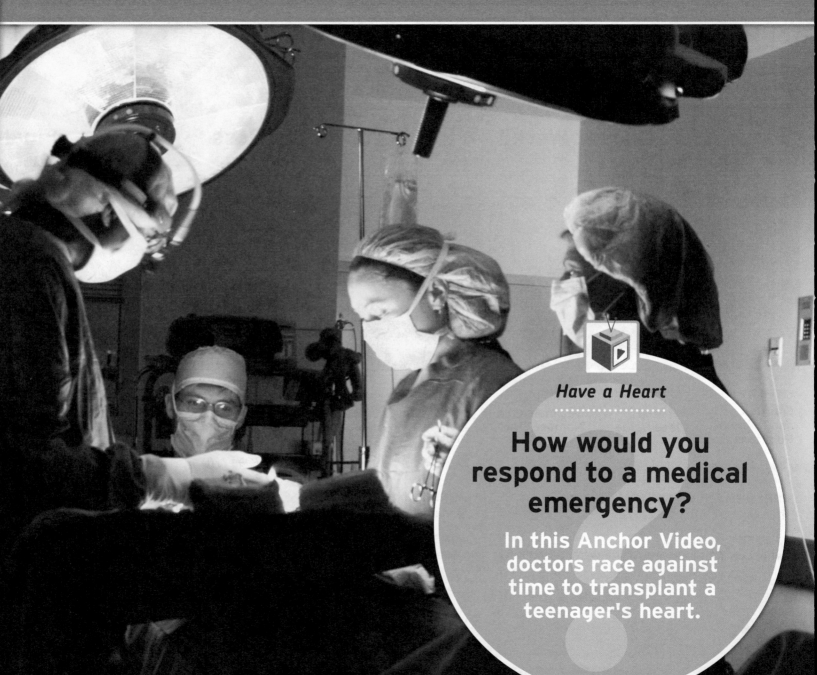

VOCABULARY

benchmark

common denominator

common numerator

equivalent

inverse operation

multiple

simplest form

unknown

Have a Heart

How would you respond to a medical emergency?

In this Anchor Video, doctors race against time to transplant a teenager's heart.

Math in Health and Medicine

In this Block, you will explore how math is used in health science careers.

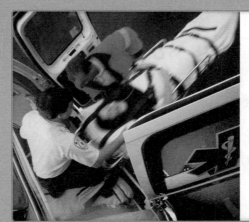

Do you work well under pressure?

Emergency
MEDICAL TECHNICIANS (EMT)

respond to **911** calls. They provide emergency medical care to patients on the way to the hospital.

Doctors

top most lists of highest-paid professions. It takes at least **10–12 years** of school and internships to get a license. There are more than **50** types, or specialties, of doctors.

REGISTERED
Nurses

treat patients in schools, doctors' offices, and even summer camps. They calculate doses of medicine, such as **500 cc** of fluids.

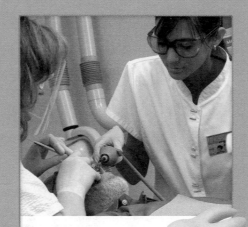

Dental
ASSISTANTS

make appointments, keep records, and even help clean teeth. This field is expected to grow **31%** by **2020**.

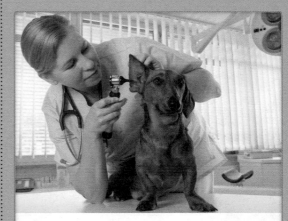

Veterinarians

care for all types of animals, from crocodiles to pet hamsters. About **1 in 4** work more than **50 hours** per week.

BLOCK 5

LESSON 1

Block Preview

> **Think about the Anchor Video and answer this question.**

If you were part of a transplant team, which job would you want?

> **Explain your thinking.**

I would want to _____

because _____

_____

_____

LESSON 2

Which Does Not Belong?

> **Circle the fraction that does not belong.**

$$\frac{6}{12} \qquad \frac{9}{18} \qquad \frac{3}{4} \qquad \frac{4}{8}$$

> **How do you know which fraction does not belong?**

I know _____ does not belong

because _____

_____

LESSON 3

Brain Teaser

> **Solve this riddle.**

• I am a fraction equivalent to $\frac{1}{2}$.

• My denominator is less than 10.

• My numerator is greater than 3.

What fraction am I? _____

> **Explain your reasoning.**

The fraction is _____ because

_____

_____

_____

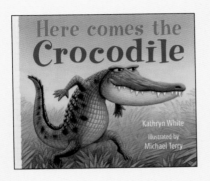

Here comes the **Crocodile**

Kathryn White
Illustrated by
Michael Terry

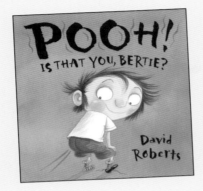

POOH!
IS THAT YOU, BERTIE?

David
Roberts

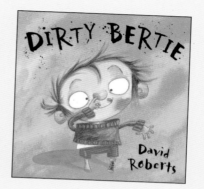

DIRTY BERTIE

David
Roberts

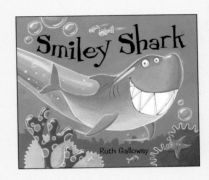

Smiley Shark

Ruth Galloway

More books to make you feel super from Little Tiger Press

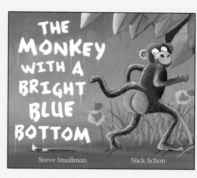

THE
**MONKEY
WITH A
BRIGHT
BLUE
BOTTOM**

Steve Smallman   Nick Schon

QUIET!

Paul Bright
illustrated by
Guy Parker-Rees

For information regarding any of the above
titles or for our catalogue, please contact us:
Little Tiger Press, 1 The Coda Centre, 189 Munster Road,
London SW6 6AW Tel: 020 7385 6333
Fax: 020 7385 7333 E-mail: info@littletiger.co.uk
www.littletigerpress.com

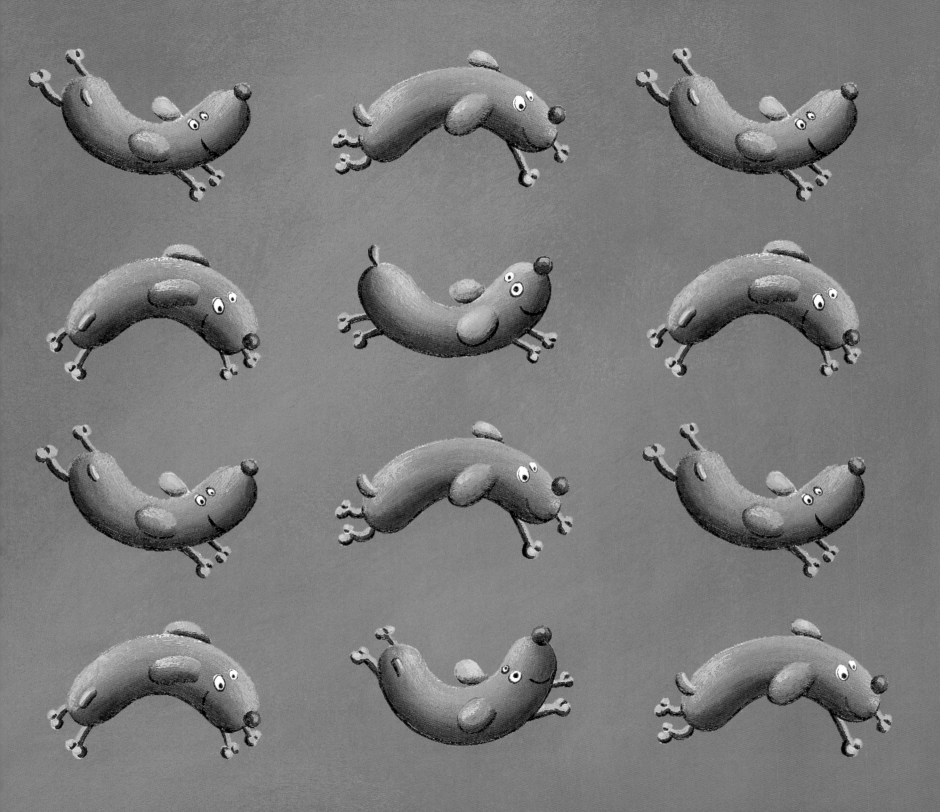

LESSON 4

Find the Pattern

> Find the rule. Then, write three fractions in the circle using the rule.

$\frac{7}{9}$ $\frac{3}{8}$ $\frac{10}{24}$ $\frac{3}{5}$

$\frac{4}{10}$ $\frac{1}{6}$

$\frac{6}{8}$ $\frac{5}{12}$ $\frac{6}{16}$ $\frac{4}{5}$

> **Why do the fractions you wrote belong in the circle?**

I think _____ , _____ ,

and _____ belong in the circle

because _____

LESSON 5

Who's Right?

> Ann says that $\frac{3}{10}$ is less than $\frac{6}{8}$.

Tarik says that $\frac{3}{10}$ is greater than $\frac{6}{8}$.

Who's right? _____

> **Who is right? How do you know?**

I know _____ is right

because _____

_____

_____

_____

> In this Topic, you learned reasoning strategies for comparing fractions.

I know that $\frac{4}{5}$ is greater than $\frac{4}{12}$ because fifths are greater than twelfths.

I can prove this with fraction pieces.

BLOCK 5

> WORKED EXAMPLE
> TRY IT
> PRACTICE

STEP 1 Compare unit fractions.

$$\frac{1}{6} \boxed{>} \frac{1}{8}$$

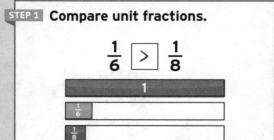

STEP 2 Compare fractions with common numerators.

$$\frac{3}{4} \boxed{>} \frac{3}{8}$$

STEP 3 Compare fractions with common denominators.

$$\frac{3}{12} \boxed{<} \frac{5}{12}$$

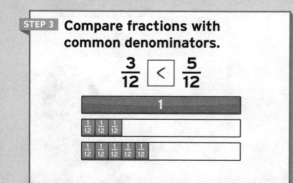

1

STEP 1 Compare unit fractions.

$$\frac{1}{4} \boxed{} \frac{1}{2}$$

Strategy: _____

STEP 2 Compare fractions with common numerators.

$$\frac{5}{6} \boxed{} \frac{5}{12}$$

Strategy: _____

STEP 3 Compare fractions with common denominators.

$$\frac{4}{6} \boxed{} \frac{5}{6}$$

Strategy: _____

2

STEP 1 Compare unit fractions.

$$\frac{1}{16} \boxed{} \frac{1}{12}$$

Strategy: _____

STEP 2 Compare fractions with common numerators.

$$\frac{3}{16} \boxed{} \frac{3}{8}$$

Strategy: _____

STEP 3 Compare fractions with common denominators.

$$\frac{5}{12} \boxed{} \frac{7}{12}$$

Strategy: _____

3

$$\frac{1}{12} \quad \Box \quad \frac{1}{3}$$

Strategy: _____

4

$$\frac{3}{8} \quad \Box \quad \frac{3}{4}$$

Strategy: _____

5

$$\frac{2}{3} \quad \Box \quad \frac{2}{4}$$

Strategy: _____

6

$$\frac{11}{16} \quad \Box \quad \frac{6}{16}$$

Strategy: _____

7

$$\frac{1}{5} \quad \Box \quad \frac{3}{5}$$

Strategy: _____

8

$$\frac{1}{10} \quad \Box \quad \frac{1}{100}$$

Strategy: _____

9

$$\frac{3}{16} \quad \Box \quad \frac{15}{16}$$

Strategy: _____

10

$$\frac{5}{7} \quad \Box \quad \frac{5}{8}$$

Strategy: _____

11

$$\frac{4}{20} \quad \Box \quad \frac{20}{20}$$

Strategy: _____

12

$$\frac{1}{5} \quad \Box \quad \frac{1}{6}$$

Strategy: _____

EXIT Ticket

> **Answer this question.**

Mario and Lana compared these fractions.

Mario	Lana
$\frac{7}{11} > \frac{7}{12}$	$\frac{7}{11} < \frac{7}{12}$

Who is correct? _____

> **Explain who is correct and why.**

_____ is correct because

_____

_____

_____

_____

I can compare fractions with common numerators by looking at the denominators.

BLOCK **5**

TOPIC 3

TOPIC 2

TOPIC 1

SCORE ⓪ ① ②

Strategies for Comparing Fractions 7 ▶

Identify Fractions Equivalent to $\frac{1}{2}$

> WORKED EXAMPLE | > TRY IT | > PRACTICE

STEP 1 Build fraction rows equivalent to $\frac{1}{2}$.

$\frac{1}{2}$	$\frac{1}{2}$
$\frac{1}{4}$ $\frac{1}{4}$	$\frac{2}{4}$
$\frac{1}{6}$ $\frac{1}{6}$ $\frac{1}{6}$	$\frac{3}{6}$
$\frac{1}{8}$ $\frac{1}{8}$ $\frac{1}{8}$ $\frac{1}{8}$	$\frac{4}{8}$
$\frac{1}{10}$ $\frac{1}{10}$ $\frac{1}{10}$ $\frac{1}{10}$ $\frac{1}{10}$	$\frac{5}{10}$

STEP 2 Find the rule.

Rule: $\dfrac{\text{numerator} = \text{denominator} \div 2}{\text{denominator} = \text{numerator} \times 2}$

STEP 3 Write fractions equivalent to $\frac{1}{2}$ with a given denominator.

$$\frac{1}{2} = \frac{\boxed{9}}{18}$$

Rule: $\dfrac{\text{numerator} = \text{denominator} \div 2}{\underline{18} \div \underline{2} = \underline{9}}$

STEP 4 Write fractions equivalent to $\frac{1}{2}$ with a given numerator.

$$\frac{1}{2} = \frac{15}{\boxed{30}}$$

Rule: $\dfrac{\text{denominator} = \text{numerator} \times 2}{\underline{15} \times \underline{2} = \underline{30}}$

1

STEP 1 Identify the rule.

$$\frac{1}{2} = \frac{\boxed{}}{22}$$

Rule: _____

STEP 2 Use the rule to name the fraction.

_____ ÷ _____ = _____

STEP 3 Identify the rule.

$$\frac{1}{2} = \frac{21}{\boxed{}}$$

Rule: _____

STEP 4 Use the rule to name the fraction.

_____ × _____ = _____

2

STEP 1 Identify the rule.

$$\frac{1}{2} = \frac{\boxed{}}{24}$$

Rule: _____

STEP 2 Use the rule to name the fraction.

_____ ÷ _____ = _____

STEP 3 Identify the rule.

$$\frac{1}{2} = \frac{10}{\boxed{}}$$

Rule: _____

STEP 4 Use the rule to name the fraction.

_____ × _____ = _____

equivalent *(adj)* having the same meaning or having the same amount

3

$$\frac{\square}{14} = \frac{1}{2}$$

4

$$\frac{1}{2} = \frac{\square}{18}$$

5

$$\frac{1}{2} = \frac{\square}{38}$$

6

$$\frac{\square}{30} = \frac{1}{2}$$

7

$$\frac{20}{\square} = \frac{1}{2}$$

8

$$\frac{1}{2} = \frac{16}{\square}$$

9

$$\frac{50}{\square} = \frac{1}{2}$$

10

$$\frac{\square}{36} = \frac{1}{2}$$

11

$$\frac{250}{\square} = \frac{1}{2}$$

12

$$\frac{1}{2} = \frac{\square}{250}$$

EXIT Ticket

BLOCK 5

> **Complete the equations.**

$$\frac{1}{2} = \frac{\square}{40}$$

$$\frac{1}{2} = \frac{8}{\square}$$

> **Explain how you found the answer to one of the equations.**

I found the answer to $\frac{1}{2} = $ _____

by _____

_____

_____

When I see a fraction with a denominator that is two times the numerator, I know it is equivalent to $\frac{1}{2}$.

TOPIC 3

TOPIC 2

TOPIC 1

SCORE ⓪ ① ②

Strategies for Comparing Fractions 9

LESSON 3
CONCEPT

Use Benchmarks to Compare Fractions

> WORKED EXAMPLE

STEP 1 Compare fractions to 1.

$$\frac{5}{4} \boxed{>} \frac{7}{8}$$

Strategy: _Compare to 1_

$\frac{5}{4} > \frac{4}{4}$	$\frac{7}{8} < \frac{8}{8}$
$\frac{5}{4} > 1$	$\frac{7}{8} < 1$

STEP 2 Verify with fraction pieces.

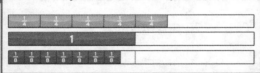

STEP 3 Compare fractions to $\frac{1}{2}$.

$$\frac{7}{16} \boxed{<} \frac{5}{8}$$

Strategy: _Compare to $\frac{1}{2}$_

$\frac{7}{16} < \frac{8}{16}$	$\frac{5}{8} > \frac{4}{8}$
$\frac{7}{16} < \frac{1}{2}$	$\frac{5}{8} > \frac{1}{2}$

STEP 4 Verify with fraction pieces.

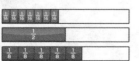

> TRY IT

1

STEP 1 Compare fractions.

$$\frac{4}{3} \boxed{} \frac{5}{6}$$

Strategy: _____

STEP 2 Verify with fraction pieces.

STEP 3 Compare fractions.

$$\frac{5}{12} \boxed{} \frac{7}{8}$$

Strategy: _____

STEP 4 Verify with fraction pieces.

> PRACTICE

2

STEP 1 Compare fractions.

$$\frac{3}{2} \boxed{} \frac{1}{3}$$

Strategy: _____

STEP 2 Verify with fraction pieces.

STEP 3 Compare fractions.

$$\frac{3}{4} \boxed{} \frac{1}{12}$$

Strategy: _____

STEP 4 Verify with fraction pieces.

benchmark *(n)* familiar numbers that you use to make comparisons and estimates

3

$$\frac{3}{2} \square \frac{2}{3}$$

Strategy: _____

4

$$\frac{7}{10} \square \frac{25}{100}$$

Strategy: _____

5

$$\frac{5}{16} \square \frac{3}{4}$$

Strategy: _____

6

$$\frac{2}{3} \square \frac{1}{6}$$

Strategy: _____

7

$$\frac{11}{12} \square \frac{5}{4}$$

Strategy: _____

8

$$\frac{7}{12} \square \frac{7}{16}$$

Strategy: _____

9

$$\frac{12}{15} \square \frac{15}{12}$$

Strategy: _____

10

$$\frac{25}{100} \square \frac{35}{40}$$

Strategy: _____

EXIT Ticket

BLOCK **5**

> Complete the inequality.

$$\frac{7}{8} \square \frac{15}{40}$$

Strategy: _____

 TOPIC 3

 TOPIC 2

> How did you begin working on this problem?

I began working on this problem

by _____

_____

_____

_____

_____

_____

 TOPIC 1

SCORE ⓪ ① ②

Strategies for Comparing Fractions **11**

BLOCK 5

In fractions equal to $\frac{1}{2}$, the numerator equals half of the denominator.

RULES

Fraction Grab (Level 1)

What You Need

- *mSpace* pages 12–15.
- fraction cards

What to Know

- Shuffle the cards and deal them out equally.
- The player whose card is greater than $\frac{1}{2}$ collects both cards.

How to Win

- If both players' cards are greater than, less than, or equal to $\frac{1}{2}$, players each turn over a new card.
- The winner is the player with the most cards after 10 rounds.

> HOW TO PLAY

STEP 1 Each player turns over one card.

$$\frac{3}{4} \qquad \frac{3}{8}$$

Player A   Player B

STEP 2 Both players record the fractions.

PLAYER A
FRACTION
$$\frac{3}{4}$$

PLAYER B
FRACTION
$$\frac{3}{8}$$

STEP 3 Players compare their fractions to $\frac{1}{2}$.

COMPARE THE FRACTION TO $\frac{1}{2}$ USING >, <, OR =
$$\frac{3}{4} > \frac{1}{2}$$

COMPARE THE FRACTION TO $\frac{1}{2}$ USING >, <, OR =
$$\frac{3}{8} < \frac{1}{2}$$

STEP 4 The player with the fraction greater than $\frac{1}{2}$ captures both cards.

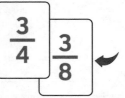

Player A   Player B

RECORDING SHEET

Fraction Grab (Level 1)

> Record your inequalities and your partner's inequalities.
> Optional: Use page 15 for calculations.

ROUND	PLAYER A		PLAYER B	
	FRACTION	COMPARE THE FRACTION TO $\frac{1}{2}$ USING $>$, $<$, OR $=$	FRACTION	COMPARE THE FRACTION TO $\frac{1}{2}$ USING $>$, $<$, OR $=$
1				
2				
3				
4				
5				
6				
7				
8				
9				
10				
	TOTAL NUMBER OF CARDS		TOTAL NUMBER OF CARDS	

BLOCK 5 > TOPIC 1
LESSON 4

RECORDING SHEET
Fraction Grab (Level 1)

> Record your inequalities and your partner's inequalities.
> Optional: Use page 15 for calculations.

BLOCK 5

ROUND	PLAYER A FRACTION	COMPARE THE FRACTION TO $\frac{1}{2}$ USING >, <, OR =	PLAYER B FRACTION	COMPARE THE FRACTION TO $\frac{1}{2}$ USING >, <, OR =
1				
2				
3				
4				
5				
6				
7				
8				
9				
10				
TOTAL NUMBER OF CARDS			TOTAL NUMBER OF CARDS	

> **Optional: Use this page for calculations.**

> **Answer this question.**

Player A's card is $\frac{3}{4}$ and Player B's card is $\frac{5}{12}$. How do you know who wins the round?

Player _____ wins the round

because _____

_____

_____

_____

_____

SCORE ⓪ ① ②

CAREER EXPLORATION

> **Forensic scientists use math to help solve crimes.**

How might forensic scientists use fractions to analyze evidence samples?

TOPIC 3

TOPIC 2

TOPIC 1

LESSON 5
PROBLEM SOLVING

Order Fractions to Solve Problems

BLOCK 5

> **WORKED EXAMPLE**

STEP 1 **Analyze the problem.**

Five people donated blood. They gave $\frac{3}{10}$ pint, $\frac{5}{4}$ pint, $\frac{3}{8}$ pint, $\frac{11}{16}$ pint, and $\frac{9}{16}$ pint. Put the amounts in order from least to greatest.

$$\frac{3}{10} \quad \frac{5}{4} \quad \frac{3}{8} \quad \frac{11}{16} \quad \frac{9}{16}$$

STEP 2 **Compare with common features.**

$$\frac{3}{10} < \frac{3}{8} \qquad \frac{9}{16} < \frac{11}{16}$$

$$\frac{5}{4}$$

_____ _____ _____ _____

STEP 3 **Compare with benchmarks.**

$$\frac{3}{8} < \frac{1}{2} \qquad \frac{9}{16} > \frac{1}{2}$$

$$\frac{3}{10} \qquad \frac{3}{8} \qquad \frac{9}{16} \qquad \frac{11}{16} \qquad \frac{5}{4}$$

_____ _____ _____ _____ _____

STEP 4 **Check your work.**

> **TRY IT**

1

STEP 1 **Analyze the problem.**

Emergency responders record the distances traveled for each incident. The distances are $\frac{2}{10}$ mi, $\frac{5}{6}$ mi, $\frac{5}{4}$ mi, $\frac{5}{8}$ mi, and $\frac{2}{5}$ mi. Put the amounts in order from least to greatest.

STEP 2 **Compare with common features.**

STEP 3 **Compare with benchmarks.**

_____ _____ _____ _____ _____

STEP 4 **Check your work.**

> **PRACTICE**

2

STEP 1 **Analyze the problem.**

Ana measures the amount of formula a baby drinks each hour. The amounts are $\frac{5}{16}$ oz, $1\frac{15}{16}$ oz, $1\frac{3}{4}$ oz, $2\frac{1}{8}$ oz, and $\frac{13}{16}$ oz. Put the amounts in order from least to greatest.

STEP 2 **Compare with common features.**

STEP 3 **Compare with benchmarks.**

_____ _____ _____ _____ _____

STEP 4 **Check your work.**

3

A doctor measured a baby's weight gain each month. The baby gained $\frac{6}{5}$ lb, $\frac{1}{4}$ lb, $\frac{7}{10}$ lb, $\frac{7}{4}$ lb, and $\frac{9}{10}$ lb. Put the amounts in order from least to greatest.

———— —— —— ——

4

An orthodontist measured the distance between Todd's two front teeth for each week that Todd had braces. The distances were $\frac{3}{5}$ mm, $\frac{11}{10}$ mm, $\frac{2}{5}$ mm, $\frac{15}{10}$ mm, and $\frac{9}{10}$ mm. Put the amounts in order from least to greatest.

———— —— —— ——

EXIT Ticket

> **Solve this problem.**

A veterinarian weighs five puppies. Their weights are $9\frac{5}{12}$ lb, $8\frac{1}{6}$ lb, $8\frac{3}{12}$ lb, $9\frac{1}{2}$ lb, and $8\frac{3}{4}$ lb. Put the weights in order from least to greatest.

———— —— —— ——

How can I use $\frac{1}{2}$ or 1 as benchmark numbers to check my answers?

SCORE ⓪ ① ②

BLOCK 5

Missing Numbers

> Fill in the boxes to make fractions equivalent to $\frac{1}{2}$. Use these numbers:

2, 3, 4, 6, 8, and 16

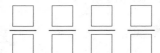

> Explain how you found fractions equivalent to $\frac{1}{2}$.

I found fractions equivalent to $\frac{1}{2}$

by _____

_____

_____

Find the Pattern

> Find the rule. Then, write three numbers in the circle using the rule.

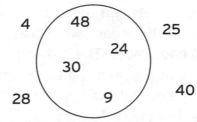

4   48   25
          24
      30
28   9   40

> Why do the numbers you wrote belong inside the circle?

The numbers _____, _____, _____

belong in the circle because _____

_____

_____

Who's Right?

> Max and Lola found two different mixed numbers for $\frac{7}{6}$.

Max	Lola
$\frac{7}{6} = 1\frac{1}{6}$	$\frac{7}{6} = 1\frac{1}{7}$

Who's right? _____

> How do you know who's right? Justify your reasoning.

_____ is right because

_____

_____

_____

Brain Teaser

> **Solve this riddle.**

- I am greater than $\frac{1}{2}$.

- I am less than $\frac{3}{4}$.

- My denominator is 8.

> **Which fraction am I?** _____

> **What was your first step in solving this riddle?**

My first step in solving this riddle

was _____

_____

Which Does Not Belong?

> **Circle the fraction that does not belong.**

$$\frac{5}{8} \qquad \frac{3}{4} \qquad \frac{9}{10} \qquad \frac{1}{3} \qquad \frac{4}{5}$$

> **How do you know which fraction does not belong?**

I know _____ does not belong

because _____

_____

> In this Topic, you learned how to rename fractions with equivalent fractions, compare fractions, and locate fractions on a number line.

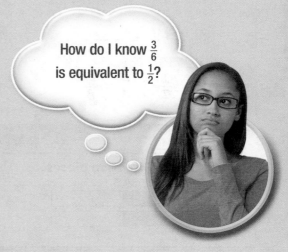

How do I know $\frac{3}{6}$ is equivalent to $\frac{1}{2}$?

You can use reasoning or think of your fraction pieces.

LESSON 1
CONCEPT

Name Equivalent Fractions

BLOCK 5

> WORKED EXAMPLE

> TRY IT

> PRACTICE

> WORKED EXAMPLE

STEP 1 Use multiplication to generate equivalent fractions.

$$\frac{1}{2} = \frac{\boxed{4}}{8}$$

$$\frac{1}{2} \times \frac{4}{4} = \frac{4}{8}$$

STEP 2 Verify with fraction pieces.

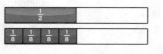

STEP 3 Use division to generate equivalent fractions.

$$\frac{4}{16} = \frac{\boxed{1}}{4}$$

$$\frac{4}{16} \div \frac{4}{4} = \frac{1}{4}$$

STEP 4 Verify with fraction pieces.

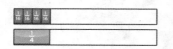

> TRY IT

1

STEP 1 Use multiplication to generate equivalent fractions.

$$\frac{2}{3} = \frac{\square}{12}$$

STEP 2 Verify with fraction pieces.

STEP 3 Use division to generate equivalent fractions.

$$\frac{6}{8} = \frac{\square}{4}$$

STEP 4 Verify with fraction pieces.

> PRACTICE

2

STEP 1 Use multiplication to generate equivalent fractions.

$$\frac{1}{3} = \frac{\square}{12}$$

STEP 2 Verify with fraction pieces.

STEP 3 Use division to generate equivalent fractions.

$$\frac{8}{16} = \frac{\square}{8}$$

STEP 4 Verify with fraction pieces.

simplest form *(adj)* when 1 is the only whole number that divides both the numerator and denominator evenly

3

$$\frac{1}{5} = \frac{\boxed{}}{15}$$

4

$$\frac{4}{20} = \frac{2}{\boxed{}}$$

5

$$\frac{9}{12} = \frac{\boxed{}}{4}$$

6

$$\frac{6}{20} = \frac{3}{\boxed{}}$$

7

$$\frac{4}{5} = \frac{\boxed{}}{20}$$

8

$$\frac{3}{10} = \frac{\boxed{}}{100}$$

EXIT Ticket

BLOCK **5**

TOPIC 3

> **Find the numerator.**

$$\frac{3}{8} = \frac{\boxed{}}{24}$$

> **Why did you multiply to find an equivalent fraction for $\frac{3}{8}$?**

TOPIC 2

I multiplied to find an equivalent

fraction because _____

_____

_____

_____

_____

TOPIC 1

I simplify by dividing the numerator and denominator to get an equivalent fraction.

SCORE ⓪ ① ②

BLOCK 5

> WORKED EXAMPLE

STEP 1 Identify a compare strategy.

$$\frac{5}{6} \ \square \ \frac{7}{10}$$

Compare Strategy: _Common Denominator_

STEP 2 Find a common denominator.

Multiples of _6_ : 6, 12, 18, 24, (30,) 36, 42, ...

Multiples of _10_ : 10, 20, (30,) 40, 50, 60, ...

STEP 3 Rename the fractions.

$$\frac{5}{6} \times \frac{5}{5} = \frac{25}{30}$$

$$\frac{7}{10} \times \frac{3}{3} = \frac{21}{30}$$

STEP 4 Compare the fractions.

$$\frac{25}{30} > \frac{21}{30}$$

$$\frac{5}{6} > \frac{7}{10}$$

> TRY IT

1

STEP 1 Identify a compare strategy.

$$\frac{3}{8} \ \square \ \frac{5}{12}$$

Compare Strategy:

_____

STEP 2 Find a common denominator.

Multiples of _____: _____

_____

Multiples of _____: _____

_____

STEP 3 Rename the fractions.

STEP 4 Compare the fractions.

> PRACTICE

2

STEP 1 Identify a compare strategy.

$$\frac{2}{3} \ \square \ \frac{3}{5}$$

Compare Strategy:

_____

STEP 2 Find a common denominator.

Multiples of _____: _____

_____

Multiples of _____: _____

_____

STEP 3 Rename the fractions.

STEP 4 Compare the fractions.

common denominator *(n)* the denominator of two or more fractions that have the same denominator

> PRACTICE

3
$$\frac{3}{8} \quad \square \quad \frac{1}{3}$$

4
$$\frac{3}{5} \quad \square \quad \frac{7}{10}$$

5
$$\frac{3}{4} \quad \square \quad \frac{2}{3}$$

6
$$\frac{7}{9} \quad \square \quad \frac{2}{3}$$

7
$$\frac{2}{7} \quad \square \quad \frac{1}{3}$$

8
$$\frac{4}{5} \quad \square \quad \frac{3}{8}$$

9
$$\frac{3}{5} \quad \square \quad \frac{4}{6}$$

10
$$\frac{9}{10} \quad \square \quad \frac{4}{5}$$

> **Compare the fractions.**

$$\frac{3}{10} \quad \square \quad \frac{2}{3}$$

TOPIC 3

> **Could you use another strategy to compare these fractions? Explain your thinking.**

I could use the strategy of

_____

because _____

_____

_____

TOPIC 2

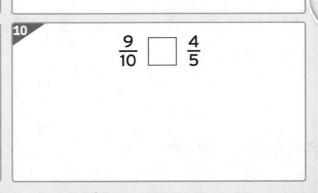

I like comparing fractions using benchmarks, because I can compare them without writing any calculations.

TOPIC 1

SCORE ⓪ ① ②

Locate Fractions on a Number Line

> WORKED EXAMPLE

> TRY IT

> PRACTICE

BLOCK 5

STEP 1 Locate halves on a number line.

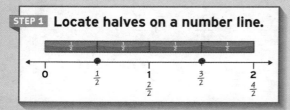

STEP 2 Locate fourths on a number line.

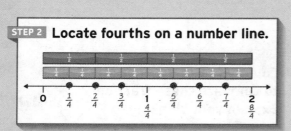

STEP 3 Locate eighths on a number line.

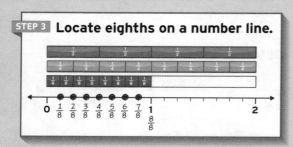

1

STEP 1 Label the number line.

Locate $\frac{7}{4}$ on a number line.

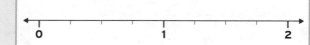

STEP 2 Locate the fraction.

STEP 3 Label the number line.

Locate $\frac{11}{6}$ on a number line.

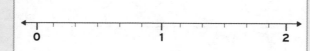

STEP 4 Locate the fraction.

2

STEP 1 Label the number line.

Locate $\frac{4}{5}$ on a number line.

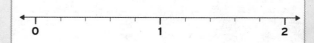

STEP 2 Locate the fraction.

STEP 3 Label the number line.

Locate $\frac{8}{9}$ on a number line.

STEP 4 Locate the fraction.

> PRACTICE

3

Locate $\frac{10}{3}$ on a number line.

4

Locate $\frac{11}{8}$ on a number line.

5

Locate $\frac{4}{3}$ on a number line.

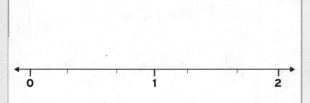

6

Locate $\frac{6}{5}$ on a number line.

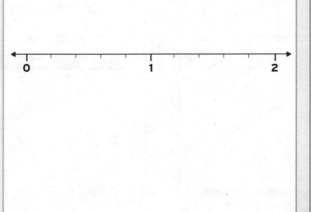

> **Solve this problem.**

Locate $\frac{11}{3}$ on a number line.

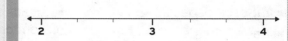

TOPIC 3

> **How do you know you correctly located $\frac{11}{3}$ on the number line?**

I know I correctly located $\frac{11}{3}$

on the number line because

_____

_____

_____

_____

_____

_____

TOPIC 2

TOPIC 1

SCORE ⓪ ① ②

Use Strategies to Compare Fractions

RULES
Fraction Grab (Level 2)

I use the benchmark strategy because it helps me compare fractions mentally.

What You Need
- *mSpace* pages 26–29
- fraction cards

What to Know
- Shuffle the cards and deal them out equally.
- If the fractions are equivalent, players turn over a second card and play again.

How to Win
- The winner is the player with the most cards.

> HOW TO PLAY

STEP 1 Each player turns over one card.

$\frac{3}{4}$	$\frac{2}{3}$
Player A	Player B

STEP 2 Players record their fractions and rename them with a common denominator.

PLAYER A	PLAYER B
FRACTION	FRACTION
$\frac{3}{4}$	$\frac{2}{3}$

STEP 3 Players compare the fractions.

PLAYER A	PLAYER B
FRACTION	FRACTION
$\frac{3}{4}$	$\frac{2}{3}$

COMPARE THE FRACTION USING >, <, OR =

$$\frac{3}{4} > \frac{2}{3}$$

STEP 4 The player with the greater fraction captures both cards.

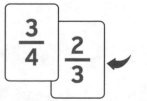

$\frac{3}{4}$	$\frac{2}{3}$
Player A	Player B

RECORDING SHEET

Fraction Grab (Level 2)

› Record your fractions, your partner's fractions, and the inequality.
Optional: Use page 29 for calculations.

ROUND	PLAYER A FRACTION	PLAYER B FRACTION	COMPARE THE FRACTION USING >, <, OR =	ROUND	PLAYER A FRACTION	PLAYER B FRACTION	COMPARE THE FRACTION USING >, <, OR =
1				11			
2				12			
3				13			
4				14			
5				15			
6				16			
7				17			
8				18			
9				19			
10				20			
					TOTAL NUMBER OF CARDS	TOTAL NUMBER OF CARDS	

RECORDING SHEET
Fraction Grab (Level 2)

> Record your fractions, your partner's fractions, and the inequality.
> Optional: Use page 29 for calculations.

BLOCK 5

ROUND	PLAYER A FRACTION	PLAYER B FRACTION	COMPARE THE FRACTION USING >, <, OR =
1			
2			
3			
4			
5			
6			
7			
8			
9			
10			

ROUND	PLAYER A FRACTION	PLAYER B FRACTION	COMPARE THE FRACTION USING >, <, OR =
11			
12			
13			
14			
15			
16			
17			
18			
19			
20			
	TOTAL NUMBER OF CARDS	TOTAL NUMBER OF CARDS	

> **Optional: Use this page for calculations.**

> **Answer this question.**

Circle the player who wins this round.

$\dfrac{3}{4}$	$\dfrac{5}{6}$
Player A	Player B

> **Explain how you know which fraction is greater.**

_____ is the greater fraction

because _____

_____

_____

SCORE ⓪ ① ②

CAREER EXPLORATION

> **Nutritionists work at hospitals to plan healthy meals for patients.**

How could a nutritionist use math to calculate the number of servings for multiple patients?

BLOCK 5

> WORKED EXAMPLE

> TRY IT

> PRACTICE

STEP 1 Analyze the problem.

What fraction is less than $\frac{2}{3}$, is greater than $\frac{1}{4}$, and has a denominator of 12?

STEP 2 Find common denominators.

$$\frac{2 \times 4}{3 \times 4} = \frac{8}{12} \qquad \frac{1 \times 3}{4 \times 3} = \frac{3}{12}$$

STEP 3 Label the fractions on the number line.

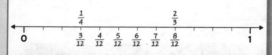

STEP 4 Solve the problem.

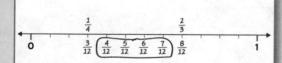

Check one: This problem has
- ☐ exactly one solution.
- ☑ more than one solution.
- ☐ no solution.

1

STEP 1 Analyze the problem.

What fraction is equivalent to $\frac{3}{4}$ and has a denominator that is two times as great as the numerator?

STEP 2 Find common denominators.

STEP 3 Label the fractions on the number line.

STEP 4 Solve the problem.

Check one: This problem has
- ☐ exactly one solution.
- ☐ more than one solution.
- ☐ no solution.

2

STEP 1 Analyze the problem.

What fraction is greater than $\frac{1}{9}$, is less than $\frac{1}{3}$, and has a denominator of 18?

STEP 2 Find common denominators.

STEP 3 Label the fractions on the number line.

STEP 4 Solve the problem.

Check one: This problem has
- ☐ exactly one solution.
- ☐ more than one solution.
- ☐ no solution.

3

What fraction is equivalent to $\frac{5}{6}$ and has a numerator that is 2 less than its denominator?

Check one: This problem has

❑ exactly one solution.

❑ more than one solution.

❑ no solution.

4

What fraction is equivalent to $\frac{1}{3}$ and has a denominator that is 3 times as great as its numerator?

Check one: This problem has

❑ exactly one solution.

❑ more than one solution.

❑ no solution.

EXIT
Ticket

BLOCK
5

TOPIC 3

> **Solve this problem.**

What fraction is greater than $\frac{3}{5}$, is less than $\frac{3}{4}$, and has a denominator of 20?

$\longleftrightarrow$
$\frac{3}{5}$ $\frac{3}{4}$

TOPIC 2

TOPIC 1

Check one: This problem has

❑ exactly one solution.

❑ more than one solution.

❑ no solution.

SCORE ⓪ ① ②

Which Does Not Belong?

> Circle a number that does not belong.

$\frac{1}{2}$ $\frac{10}{8}$ $\frac{8}{3}$ $\frac{3}{4}$ $\frac{5}{4}$

> How do you know which fraction does not belong?

_____ does not belong because

_____

_____

Number Strings

> Add these expressions mentally.

$\frac{1}{2} + \frac{5}{8} + 1\frac{1}{2} + \frac{3}{8}$

$\frac{3}{5} + \frac{1}{2} + 1\frac{1}{2} + \frac{1}{5}$

> What strategy did you use to add the expressions mentally?

To add the expressions mentally, I

_____

_____

Missing Numbers

> Find the missing numbers in the equation by solving the problem.

$1\frac{2}{3} = \frac{\square}{3} + \frac{2}{\square}$

$1\frac{2}{3} = \frac{\square}{3}$

> How did you begin working on this problem?

I began working on this problem by _____

_____

_____

LESSON 4

Make an Estimate

> **Estimate the sum of**

$$\frac{8}{9} + \frac{3}{4} + \frac{1}{3}$$

> **If someone estimated the sum to be about 1 would you agree with that person?**

I would agree/disagree because

_____

_____

LESSON 5

Brain Teaser

> **Solve this riddle.**

• I am a fraction greater than 1 and less than $\frac{6}{5}$.

• My denominator is less than 10.

• You can build me with your fraction pieces.

Which fraction am I? _____

> **How did you begin working on this riddle?**

I began working on this riddle by

_____

_____

_____

> In this Topic, you learned to add and subtract fractions and mixed numbers.

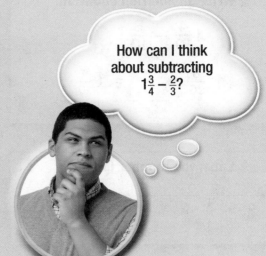

How can I think about subtracting $1\frac{3}{4} - \frac{2}{3}$?

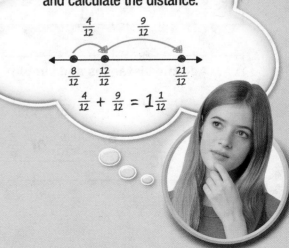

You can use an open number line to visualize and calculate the distance.

$$\frac{4}{12} \qquad \frac{9}{12}$$

$$\frac{8}{12} \qquad \frac{12}{12} \qquad \frac{21}{12}$$

$$\frac{4}{12} + \frac{9}{12} = 1\frac{1}{12}$$

> WORKED EXAMPLE

> TRY IT

> PRACTICE

STEP 1 Write an addition equation.

$$1\frac{4}{10} - \frac{8}{10}$$

$$\frac{8}{10} + \underline{\hphantom{xxx}} = 1\frac{4}{10}$$

STEP 2 Label the number line.

$$0 \quad \frac{2}{10} \quad \frac{4}{10} \quad \frac{6}{10} \quad \frac{8}{10} \quad 1 \quad 1\frac{2}{10} \quad 1\frac{4}{10} \quad 1\frac{6}{10} \quad 1\frac{8}{10} \quad 2$$
$$\frac{10}{10}$$

STEP 3 Draw and label arrows.

$$\frac{2}{10} \qquad \frac{4}{10}$$

$$0 \quad \frac{2}{10} \quad \frac{4}{10} \quad \frac{6}{10} \quad \frac{8}{10} \quad 1 \quad 1\frac{2}{10} \quad 1\frac{4}{10} \quad 1\frac{6}{10} \quad 1\frac{8}{10} \quad 2$$

STEP 4 Add the distances and simplify.

$$\frac{2}{10} + \frac{4}{10} = \frac{6}{10}$$

$$1\frac{4}{10} - \frac{8}{10} = \frac{6}{10} \text{ or } \frac{3}{5}$$

1

STEP 1 Write an addition equation.

$$2\frac{2}{6} - 1\frac{5}{6}$$

STEP 2 Label the number line.

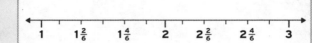

$$1 \quad 1\frac{2}{6} \quad 1\frac{4}{6} \quad 2 \quad 2\frac{2}{6} \quad 2\frac{4}{6} \quad 3$$

STEP 3 Draw and label arrows.

STEP 4 Add the distances and simplify.

$$2\frac{2}{6} - 1\frac{5}{6} = \underline{\hphantom{xxxx}}$$

2

STEP 1 Write an addition equation.

$$2\frac{8}{9} - 1\frac{3}{9}$$

STEP 2 Label the number line.

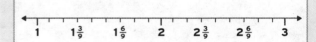

$$1 \quad 1\frac{3}{9} \quad 1\frac{6}{9} \quad 2 \quad 2\frac{3}{9} \quad 2\frac{6}{9} \quad 3$$

STEP 3 Draw and label arrows.

STEP 4 Add the distances and simplify.

$$2\frac{8}{9} - 1\frac{3}{9} = \underline{\hphantom{xxxx}}$$

3

$$1\frac{2}{5} - \frac{3}{5}$$

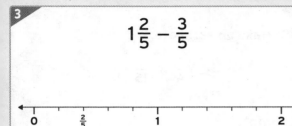

$$1\frac{2}{5} - \frac{3}{5} = \underline{\hspace{1cm}}$$

4

$$\frac{7}{9} - \frac{4}{9}$$

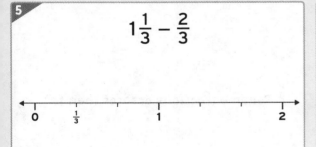

$$\frac{7}{9} - \frac{4}{9} = \underline{\hspace{1cm}}$$

5

$$1\frac{1}{3} - \frac{2}{3}$$

$$1\frac{1}{3} - \frac{2}{3} = \underline{\hspace{1cm}}$$

6

$$3\frac{1}{4} - 2\frac{2}{4}$$

$$3\frac{1}{4} - 2\frac{2}{4} = \underline{\hspace{1cm}}$$

BLOCK 5

> **Find the difference.**

$$1\frac{3}{12} - \frac{7}{12}$$

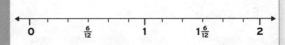

TOPIC 3

$$1\frac{3}{12} - \frac{7}{12} = \underline{\hspace{1cm}}$$

TOPIC 2

> **Explain how you found the difference using the number line.**

I found the difference using

the number line by _____

_____

_____

TOPIC 1

_____

_____

_____

_____

SCORE ⓪ ① ②

Adding and Subtracting Fractions **35**

Use Equivalence to Add Fractions

BLOCK 5

> WORKED EXAMPLE

> TRY IT

> PRACTICE

STEP 1 Make an estimate.

$$1\frac{1}{2} + \frac{2}{3}$$

Estimate: >2

STEP 2 Rename the addends.

Rename: $1\frac{1}{2} \rightarrow \frac{2}{2} + \frac{1}{2} = \frac{3}{2}$

$$\frac{3}{2} \times \frac{3}{3} = \frac{9}{6}$$

$$\frac{2}{3} \times \frac{2}{2} = \frac{4}{6}$$

STEP 3 Add the fractions.

$$\frac{9}{6} + \frac{4}{6} = \frac{13}{6}$$

STEP 4 Rename fractions greater than 1.

$$1\frac{1}{2} + \frac{2}{3} = \underline{\quad 2\frac{1}{6} \quad}$$

Is your answer reasonable? _yes_

1

STEP 1 Make an estimate.

$$2\frac{1}{5} + \frac{1}{4}$$

Estimate: _____

STEP 2 Rename the addends.

STEP 3 Add the fractions.

STEP 4 Rename fractions greater than 1.

$$2\frac{1}{5} + \frac{1}{4} = \underline{\quad\quad}$$

Is your answer reasonable? _____

2

STEP 1 Make an estimate.

$$1\frac{1}{4} + \frac{1}{16}$$

Estimate: _____

STEP 2 Rename the addends.

STEP 3 Add the fractions.

STEP 4 Rename fractions greater than 1.

$$1\frac{1}{4} + \frac{1}{16} = \underline{\quad\quad}$$

Is your answer reasonable? _____

Mixed Number *(n)* a fraction greater than 1 that includes both a whole number part and a fractional part

> **PRACTICE**

3

$$\frac{3}{5} + \frac{3}{10}$$

Estimate: _____

$$\frac{3}{5} + \frac{3}{10} = \text{_____}$$

Is your answer reasonable? _____

4

$$\frac{5}{22} + 1\frac{3}{11}$$

Estimate: _____

$$\frac{5}{22} + 1\frac{3}{11} = \text{_____}$$

Is your answer reasonable? _____

5

$$\frac{2}{15} + \frac{1}{3}$$

Estimate: _____

$$\frac{2}{15} + \frac{1}{3} = \text{_____}$$

Is your answer reasonable? _____

6

$$1\frac{1}{2} + 1\frac{2}{3}$$

Estimate: _____

$$1\frac{1}{2} + 1\frac{2}{3} = \text{_____}$$

Is your answer reasonable? _____

> **Find the sum.**

$$\frac{3}{7} + 1\frac{1}{4}$$

Estimate: _____

TOPIC 3

TOPIC 2

$$\frac{3}{7} + 1\frac{1}{4} = \text{_____}$$

> **Is your answer reasonable? How do you know?**

My answer is/is not reasonable

because _____

_____

_____

_____

TOPIC 1

SCORE ⓪ ① ②

Use an Open Number Line to Subtract

BLOCK 5

> WORKED EXAMPLE

> TRY IT

> PRACTICE

STEP 1 Make an estimate.

$$1\frac{2}{3} - \frac{5}{12}$$

Estimate: ___>1___

STEP 2 Rename the fractions.

$$1\frac{2}{3} \rightarrow \frac{3}{3} + \frac{2}{3} = \frac{5}{3} \qquad \frac{5}{3} \times \frac{4}{4} = \frac{20}{12}$$

STEP 3 Find the difference.

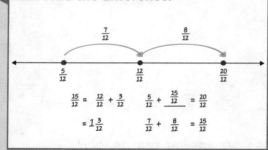

$$\frac{15}{12} = \frac{12}{12} + \frac{3}{12} \qquad \frac{5}{12} + \frac{15}{12} = \frac{20}{12}$$

$$= 1\frac{3}{12} \qquad \frac{7}{12} + \frac{8}{12} = \frac{15}{12}$$

STEP 4 Compare the difference to the estimate.

$$1\frac{2}{3} - \frac{5}{12} = \underline{\quad 1\frac{1}{4} \quad}$$

Is your answer reasonable? ___yes___

1

STEP 1 Make an estimate.

$$1\frac{7}{8} - \frac{1}{3}$$

Estimate: _____

STEP 2 Rename the fractions.

STEP 3 Find the distance.

STEP 4 Compare the difference to the estimate.

$$1\frac{7}{8} - \frac{2}{3} = \underline{\qquad}$$

Is your answer reasonable? _____

2

STEP 1 Make an estimate.

$$1\frac{3}{10} - \frac{3}{5}$$

Estimate: _____

STEP 2 Rename the fractions.

STEP 3 Find the distance.

STEP 4 Compare the difference to the estimate.

$$1\frac{3}{10} - \frac{3}{5} = \underline{\qquad}$$

Is your answer reasonable? _____

3

$$\frac{1}{3} - \frac{1}{12}$$

4

$$1\frac{7}{10} - 1\frac{1}{2}$$

5

$$1\frac{2}{5} - \frac{3}{4}$$

6

$$1 - \frac{7}{25}$$

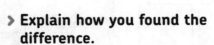

EXIT Ticket

> **Find the difference.**

$$2\frac{1}{2} - 1\frac{3}{5}$$

TOPIC 3

TOPIC 2

> **Explain how you found the difference.**

I found the difference by

_____

_____

_____

_____

_____

TOPIC 1

SCORE ⓪ ① ②

BLOCK 5

I use compare strategies to decide who has the greater sum.

RULES
Fraction Grab (Level 3)

What You Need
- *mSpace* pages 40–43
- fraction cards

What to Know
- Shuffle the cards and deal them out equally.
- If the sums are the same, players each turn over two new cards.

How to Win
- The winner is the player with the most cards.

> HOW TO PLAY

STEP 1 Each player turns over two cards.

$$\frac{5}{6} \quad \frac{1}{12}$$

Player A

$$\frac{5}{12} \quad \frac{2}{3}$$

Player B

STEP 2 Players record their fractions and rename them with a common denominator.

PLAYER A
FRACTIONS

$$\frac{5 \times 2}{6 \times 2} = \frac{10}{12} \qquad \frac{1}{12}$$

PLAYER B
FRACTIONS

$$\frac{5}{12} \qquad \frac{2 \times 4}{3 \times 4} = \frac{8}{12}$$

STEP 3 Players add their fractions and record their sum and their partner's sum.

PLAYER A	
FRACTIONS	SUM

$$\frac{5 \times 2}{6 \times 2} = \frac{10}{12} \quad \frac{1}{12} \qquad \frac{10}{12} + \frac{1}{12} = \frac{11}{12}$$

PLAYER B	
FRACTIONS	SUM

$$\frac{5}{12} \quad \frac{2 \times 4}{3 \times 4} = \frac{8}{12} \qquad \frac{5}{12} + \frac{8}{12} = \frac{13}{12}$$

STEP 4 The player with the greater sum captures all four cards.

$$\frac{5}{6} \quad \frac{1}{12}$$

Player A

$$\frac{5}{12} \quad \frac{2}{3}$$

Player B

RECORDING SHEET

Fraction Grab (Level 3)

> Record your sums and your partner's sums.
> Optional: Use page 43 for calculations.

ROUND	PLAYER A FRACTIONS	SUM	PLAYER B FRACTIONS	SUM
1				
2				
3				
4				
5				
6				
7				
8				
9				
10				
	TOTAL NUMBER OF CARDS		TOTAL NUMBER OF CARDS	

BLOCK 5

RECORDING SHEET

Fraction Grab (Level 3)

> Record your sums and your partner's sums.
Optional: Use page 43 for calculations.

ROUND	PLAYER A FRACTIONS	SUM	PLAYER B FRACTIONS	SUM
1				
2				
3				
4				
5				
6				
7				
8				
9				
10				
	TOTAL NUMBER OF CARDS		TOTAL NUMBER OF CARDS	

> **Optional: Use this space for calculations.**

> **Circle the player who wins the round.**

| $\dfrac{1}{4}$ | $\dfrac{2}{3}$ | $\dfrac{1}{4}$ | $\dfrac{2}{6}$ |

Player A · Player B

> **Can you tell which sum is greater without adding the fractions? Explain.**

_____ sum is greater

than _____ sum because

_____

_____

_____

SCORE ⓪ ① ②

TOPIC 2

CAREER EXPLORATION

> **Nurses calculate dosages of medicine for patients.**

How might a nurse use math to determine the amount of medicine a patient should take?

TOPIC 1

BLOCK 5

> WORKED EXAMPLE

| Read It! | **Read and identify the problem.** |

LAB SCIENTIST — Adam completed $\frac{1}{4}$ of his lab tests on Monday and $\frac{1}{3}$ of the tests on Tuesday. What fraction of the tests does he need to finish on Wednesday?

PROBLEM TYPE _Part-Part-Whole Problem_

| Show It! | **Represent the problem.** |

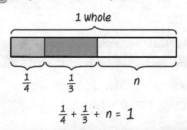

1 whole

$\frac{1}{4}$ $\frac{1}{3}$ n

$$\frac{1}{4} + \frac{1}{3} + n = 1$$

| Solve It! | **Solve the problem.** |

$$\frac{1 \times 3}{4 \times 3} = \frac{3}{12} \qquad \frac{1 \times 4}{3 \times 4} = \frac{4}{12}$$

$$\frac{3}{12} + \frac{4}{12} + n = 1 \qquad \frac{7}{12} + n = \frac{12}{12}$$

$$n = \frac{5}{12}$$

| Check It! | **Check your work.** |

> TRY IT

1

| Read It! | **Read and identify the problem.** |

VETERINARIAN — A veterinarian needs to examine 10 litters of kittens. He checks $2\frac{1}{2}$ litters one week and $6\frac{1}{10}$ litters the next week. How many litters does he still need to examine?

PROBLEM TYPE _____

| Show It! | **Represent the problem.** |

| Solve It! | **Solve the problem.** |

| Check It! | **Check your work.** |

> PRACTICE

2

| Read It! | **Read and identify the problem.** |

PHARMACIST — A pharmacist filled a prescription for Ana to take $\frac{1}{5}$ of the medicine in the morning, $\frac{1}{2}$ during lunch, and the rest at night. How much of the medicine does she take at night?

PROBLEM TYPE _____

| Show It! | **Represent the problem.** |

| Solve It! | **Solve the problem.** |

| Check It! | **Check your work.** |

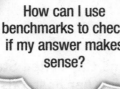

> How can I use benchmarks to check if my answer makes sense?

> PRACTICE

3

| BLOOD DONOR TECHNICIAN 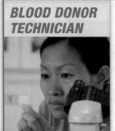 | At a clinic, $\frac{7}{16}$ of the blood donations are Type O, $\frac{3}{8}$ are Type A, and $\frac{1}{8}$ are Type B. The remaining donations are type AB. What part of the blood donations are type AB? |

PROBLEM TYPE _____

4

| ORTHOPEDIC SURGEON 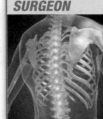 | $\frac{1}{3}$ of an orthopedic surgeon's operations are hip surgeries, $\frac{1}{4}$ are foot surgeries, $\frac{1}{6}$ are arm surgeries, and the rest are knee surgeries. What part are knee surgeries? |

PROBLEM TYPE _____

EXIT Ticket

BLOCK 5

> **Solve this problem.**

A medical assistant planned 6 hours of appointments in one day. She planned $2\frac{1}{2}$ hours for well patients and $2\frac{1}{4}$ hours for sick patients. The remaining time was for follow-up visits. How much time did she schedule for follow-up visits?

PROBLEM TYPE _____

TOPIC 3

TOPIC 2

TOPIC 1

SCORE ⓪ ① ②

Adding and Subtracting Fractions **45**

PERFORMANCE TASK

BLOCK 5

> **YOUR JOB**
> Transplant Coordinator

> **YOUR TASK**
> Match donor organs with recipients so travel times are as short as possible.

ANCHOR VIDEO CONNECTION

As the Anchor Video shows, every minute counts when a heart is transplanted.

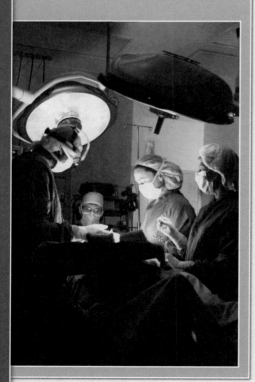

Match Organs for Transplants

> Five sets of organs are now available at hospitals around the United States. As part of the transplant team, you need to match the organs to 5 other hospitals that need them.

A EXPLORE

Draw lines on the map to connect the donor and recipient cities. Label each line with the flight time from the table. Remember, every minute counts!

KEY

⊙ Seattle	Donor city
⊙ Chicago	Recipient city
$\frac{1}{6}$	Travel time in hours between airport and hospital

Flight Times Between Cities (Hours)	Atlanta	Chicago	Los Angeles	New York	Orlando
Boston	$2\frac{1}{3}$	$2\frac{1}{5}$	$5\frac{2}{3}$	$\frac{5}{6}$	$2\frac{3}{4}$
Denver	3	$2\frac{1}{3}$	$2\frac{1}{4}$	$3\frac{3}{4}$	$3\frac{1}{2}$
Houston	$1\frac{3}{4}$	$2\frac{1}{2}$	$3\frac{1}{4}$	$3\frac{1}{3}$	$2\frac{1}{6}$
Seattle	$4\frac{5}{6}$	3	$2\frac{1}{2}$	$5\frac{1}{3}$	$5\frac{1}{2}$
Washington, DC	$1\frac{1}{2}$	$1\frac{2}{3}$	5	1	2

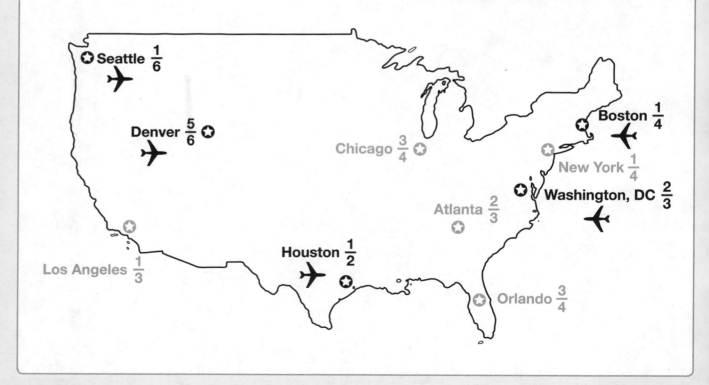

Use the map from Part A to complete Table 1. Find the total travel time for each set of organs. Try another set of city pairs in Table 2.

TABLE 1

FROM	TO	TRAVEL TIME (HOURS)	TOTAL (HOURS)
Boston		$\frac{1}{4}$ + +	
Denver		$\frac{5}{6}$ + +	
Houston		$\frac{1}{2}$ + +	
Seattle		$\frac{1}{6}$ + +	
Washington, DC		$\frac{2}{3}$ + +	

TABLE 2

FROM	TO	TRAVEL TIME (HOURS)	TOTAL (HOURS)
Boston		$\frac{1}{4}$ + +	
Denver		$\frac{5}{6}$ + +	
Houston		$\frac{1}{2}$ + +	
Seattle		$\frac{1}{6}$ + +	
Washington, DC		$\frac{2}{3}$ + +	

INTERPRET Could each donor city be matched to its closest recipient city? Why or why not?

_____

_____

REFLECT Compare your two plans for transporting the organs. Which plan is better? Explain why.

_____

_____

Evaluate

> **Rate how well you and your partner understood and completed each part of the performance task:**

Rating Scale			
None	Limited	Partial	Thorough
0	1	2	3

A Matched donor cities with recipient cities.

Me	0	1	2	3
Partner	0	1	2	3

B Calculated the total time to transport donor organs.

Me	0	1	2	3
Partner	0	1	2	3

C Answered each question accurately.

Me	0	1	2	3
Partner	0	1	2	3

EXTEND

What if only one airplane was used to transport all of the organs? Describe a route it could fly, and calculate the total flight time. Use extra paper for your work.

Scan Your Learning Strategies

Congratulations! You've completed Block 5 of *MATH 180*. For each question, fill in the circle that best describes your mindset. Then complete the sentence frames.

A CHALLENGE SEEKING

When you take on new challenges, you learn more and your brain becomes stronger and smarter.

Did you take on any challenging goals in the Brain Arcade during BLOCK 5 ?

① I did not challenge myself in the Brain Arcade. I enjoyed the games but did not worry about solving the math problems correctly.

② I tried for high scores, stars, and badges in the Brain Arcade, but I did not concentrate or work hard to achieve this goal.

③ I set a goal of earning three stars on each game, and I worked hard to achieve this goal.

I (did/did not) take on challenging goals because _____ _____ _____

B EFFORT & PRACTICE

Practice gives your brain the exercise it needs to work at its best.

Did you commit time and effort to solving *mSpace* problems during BLOCK 5 ?

① I paid only a little attention to the problems in the *mSpace*.

② I solved many of the problems, but I let my partner or the teacher solve the more difficult or challenging problems.

③ I worked with partners or by myself to solve every math problem in the *mSpace*, and I made sure I understood and corrected any mistakes.

I spent (little/some/a lot of) time on practice problems because _____ _____ _____

C PERSISTENCE

When you keep trying to solve difficult problems, connections build up in your brain over time.

What did you do when you struggled to learn a BLOCK 5 math concept?

① I quickly gave up trying to learn the concept.

② Sometimes I kept trying or asked a classmate or teacher for help.

③ I kept trying as much as possible and didn't give up. I reviewed earlier lessons, I studied examples of solutions, and I asked for help when I needed it.

I (never/sometimes/often) gave up on math problems because _____ _____ _____

D LEARNING FROM MISTAKES AND FEEDBACK

Mistakes can be an opportunity to grow and stretch your "brain muscles."

What did you do when you made a mistake on a BLOCK 5 math problem?

① I made a joke or excuse, and then I forgot about the mistake.

② I promised myself I would do better, but took few other steps to improve.

③ I reviewed and corrected the mistake, and then tried to solve a similar problem correctly.

I responded to my mistakes by _____ _____ _____

Score Your Mindset

> **Add up all the numbers that you selected (1, 2, or 3.) Then read the feedback in the chart.**

TOTAL CHECKS

If your total score was: *You were in the:*

6 or less

Fixed Mindset Zone

You were in the Fixed Mindset Zone this time. Your mindset may have held you back from doing your best.

7–10

Mixed Mindset Zone

You were in the Mixed Mindset Zone this time. You may have used some Growth Mindset thinking, but in other ways you may have held yourself back.

11 or more

Growth Mindset Zone

You were in the Growth Mindset Zone this time. You used strategies that will help you grow your brain and get smarter.

> **How can you develop a Growth Mindset?**

- Read the statements in the Mindset Scan again.
- Make a plan to help you choose the third statement in each category when you take a scan like this one again. Include specific goals in your plan.
- Review your plan as you study. Try to meet the goals you set for yourself.

Brain Boosting

> **What will you do to help your brain stay in the Growth Mindset Zone?**

I will focus on:

- ☐ Challenge-seeking
- ☐ Effort and practice
- ☐ Persistence
- ☐ Learning from mistakes

What everyone in the astronaut corps shares in common is not gender or ethnic background, but motivation, perseverance, and desire.

Ellen Ochoa
NASA astronaut and administrator

What will I do?

_____
_____
_____

Who will help me?

_____
_____
_____

When will I do it?

_____
_____
_____

How will this help me to grow?

_____
_____
_____

VOCABULARY

array

Distributive Property

divisible

inequality

mixed number

product

quotient

variable

Destination: Mars

Have you ever dreamed of traveling to another planet?

In this Anchor Video, scientists design, launch, and successfully land a rover on Mars to explore its surface.

Math in Exploration

In this Block, you will explore how math is used in science and engineering careers.

Meteorologists

study weather and climate changes over time. They use advanced **equations** and **grids** to predict the weather.

FOOD
Scientists

analyze food we eat and search for new food sources. They even come up with solutions to storing food—both on Earth and in space!

Since **1959**, only about **350** people have been chosen by NASA to become

Astronauts.

What's next for this elite group? NASA hopes to send astronauts to visit a near-Earth asteroid by **2030**!

OPTICAL
Engineers

created the lens for the Hubble Telescope, which takes photos of stars deep in outer space. At first, the lens was off by only $\frac{1}{50}$ of a human hair, and the images were not clear. The lens was fixed in outer space.

MECHANICAL
Engineers

use physics to design, test, and build machines and engines for space travel. To escape Earth's gravity, a spaceship must travel **25,000 miles per hour**.

Fraction Multiplication and Division **49**

BLOCK 6

LESSON 1
Block Preview

> Think about the Anchor Video and answer this question.

Which part of a mission to Mars would you want to work on?

> Explain your thinking.

I would want to _____

because _____

_____

_____

LESSON 2
Build It

> Create fractions with values between 1 and 3 using these numbers.

$\boxed{3}$ $\boxed{4}$ $\boxed{5}$ $\boxed{8}$

____ ____ ____ ____

> Explain how you know your fractions are between 1 and 3.

I know my fractions are between

1 and 3 because _____

_____

_____

LESSON 3
Missing Numbers

> Find the missing numbers in the equations.

- $\frac{1}{4}$ of 20 is _____.

- $\frac{1}{2}$ of _____ is 18.

- _____ of 15 is 3.

> What do you know about the word "of" that helped you solve this problem?

I know that the word "of" _____

_____

_____

LESSON 4

Brain Teaser

> Complete the puzzle.

$\frac{1}{3}$	×		=	$\frac{1}{12}$
×	■	×	■	×
	×	$\frac{1}{2}$	=	
=	■	=	■	=
$\frac{1}{15}$	×		=	

> How did you start solving this puzzle?

I started solving the puzzle by

_____

_____

_____

LESSON 5

Tell Me All That You Can

> About $\frac{1}{5}$ of 30.

• _____

• _____

• _____

> Li said, "I can multiply to find $\frac{1}{5}$ of 30." Do you agree with Li?

I agree/disagree because _____

_____

_____

> In this Topic, you learned to multiply whole numbers by unit fractions and unit fractions by unit fractions.

How do I find $\frac{1}{2}$ of $\frac{1}{4}$ without using fraction pieces?

I rewrite it as multiplication. Then I multiply the numerators and denominators to get the product.

$$\frac{1}{2} \times \frac{1}{4} = \frac{1}{8}$$

LESSON 1
CONCEPT

Model Parts of a Set as Fractions

BLOCK 6

> WORKED EXAMPLE   > TRY IT   > PRACTICE

STEP 1 Divide the set into equal parts.

$\frac{3}{4}$ of 16

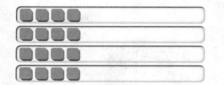

There are ___4___ rows.

STEP 2 Name one part of the set.

$\frac{1}{4}$ of 16 = ___4___

STEP 3 Name another part of the set.

$\frac{2}{4}$ of 16 = ___8___

STEP 4 Name the chosen part of the set.

$\frac{3}{4}$ of 16 = ___12___

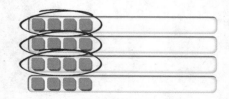

1

STEP 1 Divide the set into equal parts.

$\frac{4}{5}$ of 25

There are _____ rows.

STEP 2 Name one part of the set.

$\frac{1}{5}$ of 25 = _____

STEP 3 Name another part of the set.

$\frac{2}{5}$ of 25 = _____

STEP 4 Name the chosen part of the set.

$\frac{4}{5}$ of 25 = _____

2

STEP 1 Divide the set into equal parts.

$\frac{5}{6}$ of 24

There are _____ rows.

STEP 2 Name one part of the set.

$\frac{1}{6}$ of 24 = _____

STEP 3 Name another part of the set.

$\frac{2}{6}$ of 24 = _____

STEP 4 Name the chosen part of the set.

$\frac{5}{6}$ of 24 = _____

array *(n)* an arrangement of objects or numbers in rows and columns; can be used to represent multiplication or division

> **PRACTICE**

3

$\frac{4}{9}$ of 18

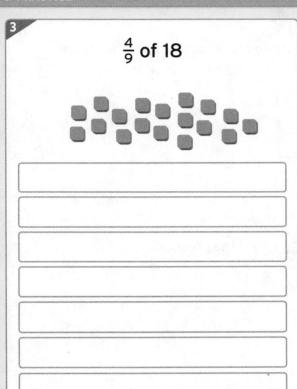

[blank boxes]

$\frac{4}{9}$ of 18 = _____

4

$\frac{7}{8}$ of 16

[array of squares]

[blank boxes]

$\frac{7}{8}$ of 16 = _____

> **Solve this problem.**

$\frac{3}{5}$ of 20

[array of squares]

[blank boxes]

$\frac{3}{5}$ of 20 = _____

> **How does drawing an array help you solve this problem?**

Drawing an array helps me solve

this problem because _____

_____

_____

_____

SCORE ⓪ ① ②

TOPIC 3

TOPIC 2

TOPIC 1

> WORKED EXAMPLE

> TRY IT

> PRACTICE

STEP 1 Replace "of" with multiplication.

$\frac{1}{3}$ of 5

$\frac{1}{3} \times 5$

STEP 2 Find the product.

$5 \times \frac{1}{3} = \frac{5}{3}$

STEP 3 Rename the product.

$\frac{5}{3} = \frac{3}{3} + \frac{2}{3}$

$= 1\frac{2}{3}$

$\frac{1}{3}$ of 5 = _____ $1\frac{2}{3}$

1

STEP 1 Replace "of" with multiplication.

$\frac{1}{6}$ of 15

STEP 2 Find the product.

STEP 3 Rename the product.

$\frac{1}{6}$ of 15 = _____

2

STEP 1 Replace "of" with multiplication.

$\frac{1}{3}$ of 4

STEP 2 Find the product.

STEP 3 Rename the product.

$\frac{1}{3}$ of 4 = _____

BLOCK 6

Commutative Property of Multiplication (n)
Changing the order of the factors does not change the product.

3

$\frac{1}{4}$ of 5

4

$\frac{1}{6}$ of 7

5

$\frac{1}{8}$ of 20

6

$\frac{1}{3}$ of 14

BLOCK
6

TOPIC 3

> **Find the product.**

$\frac{1}{5}$ of 7

TOPIC 2

> **How did you find the product?**

I found the product by _____

_____

_____

_____ TOPIC 1

_____

_____

_____

SCORE ⓪ ① ②

BLOCK 6

> WORKED EXAMPLE

STEP 1 Multiply $\frac{1}{2} \times \frac{1}{4}$ using fraction pieces.

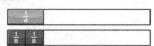

$\frac{1}{2} \times \frac{1}{4} = \underline{\frac{1}{8}}$

STEP 2 Multiply $\frac{1}{3} \times \frac{1}{4}$ using fraction pieces.

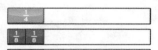

$\frac{1}{3} \times \frac{1}{4} = \underline{\frac{1}{12}}$

STEP 3 Multiply $\frac{1}{4} \times \frac{1}{4}$ using fraction pieces.

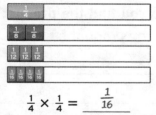

$\frac{1}{4} \times \frac{1}{4} = \underline{\frac{1}{16}}$

STEP 4 Write a rule for multiplying unit fractions.

The numerator is the _product_ of the _numerators_ .

The denominator is the _product_ of the _denominators_ .

> TRY IT

1

STEP 1 Make an estimate.

$$\frac{1}{2} \times \frac{1}{8}$$

Estimate: _____

STEP 2 Use the rule to find the product.

$$\frac{1}{2} \times \frac{1}{8} = \underline{\hspace{2cm}}$$

STEP 3 Compare the product to the estimate.

Is your answer reasonable? _____

STEP 4 Verify with fraction pieces.

> PRACTICE

2

STEP 1 Make an estimate.

$$\frac{1}{5} \times \frac{1}{2}$$

Estimate: _____

STEP 2 Use the rule to find the product.

$$\frac{1}{5} \times \frac{1}{2} = \underline{\hspace{2cm}}$$

STEP 3 Compare the product to the estimate.

Is your answer reasonable? _____

STEP 4 Verify with fraction pieces.

unit fraction (n) One of the parts from an equally divided whole; its numerator is always 1.

3

$$\frac{1}{8} \times \frac{1}{2}$$

Estimate: _____

Is your answer reasonable? _____

4

$$\frac{1}{6} \times \frac{1}{2}$$

Estimate: _____

Is your answer reasonable? _____

5

$$\frac{1}{10} \times \frac{1}{100}$$

Estimate: _____

Is your answer reasonable? _____

6

$$\frac{1}{100} \times \frac{1}{5}$$

Estimate: _____

Is your answer reasonable? _____

7

$$\frac{1}{5} \times \frac{1}{10}$$

Estimate: _____

Is your answer reasonable? _____

8

$$\frac{1}{3} \times \frac{1}{5}$$

Estimate: _____

Is your answer reasonable? _____

9

$$\frac{1}{10} \times \frac{1}{12}$$

Estimate: _____

Is your answer reasonable? _____

10

$$\frac{1}{8} \times \frac{1}{8}$$

Estimate: _____

Is your answer reasonable? _____

EXIT Ticket

BLOCK **6**

TOPIC 3

> **Find the product.**

$$\frac{1}{12} \times \frac{1}{3}$$

Estimate: _____

> **Is your product reasonable? Explain how you know.**

My product is/is not reasonable

because _____

_____

_____

_____

_____

_____

_____

TOPIC 2

TOPIC 1

When multiplying unit fractions, the numerator of the product is always 1.

SCORE ⓪ ① ②

Use Reasoning to Compare Products

To get the lesser fraction, I want the greatest possible denominator.

RULES

Less Is More (Level 1)

What You Need
- *mSpace* pages 58–61
- number cubes (green, 1–6)

What to Know
- If a 1 is rolled, roll again.
- After each round, the player with the lesser product gets a point.
- Players record their partner's product.

How to Win
- The winner is the player with the most points after five rounds.

> HOW TO PLAY

STEP 1 Roll the number cube three times.

Player A

Player B

STEP 2 Create two fractions by choosing two numbers.

Player A

NUMBERS ROLLED			MULTIPLY THE FRACTIONS
2	5	4	$\frac{1}{4} \times \frac{1}{5}$

Player B

NUMBERS ROLLED			MULTIPLY THE FRACTIONS
6	3	2	$\frac{1}{6} \times \frac{1}{3}$

STEP 3 Multiply your fractions and record your product.

Player A

MY PRODUCT
$\frac{1}{20}$

Player B

MY PRODUCT
$\frac{1}{18}$

STEP 4 Compare your product with your partner's.

Player A

COMPARE THE FRACTIONS USING >, <, OR =	MY POINTS
$\frac{1}{20} < \frac{1}{18}$	1

Player B

COMPARE THE FRACTIONS USING >, <, OR =	MY POINTS
$\frac{1}{18} > \frac{1}{20}$	0

RECORDING SHEET

Less Is More (Level 1)

> Record your fractions and products and your partner's products.
Optional: Use the grid paper on page 61 to multiply.

ROUND	NUMBERS ROLLED	MULTIPLY THE FRACTIONS	MY PRODUCT	MY PARTNER'S PRODUCT	COMPARE THE FRACTIONS USING >, <, OR =	MY POINTS
1		$\dfrac{1}{\square} \times \dfrac{1}{\square}$				
2		$\dfrac{1}{\square} \times \dfrac{1}{\square}$				
3		$\dfrac{1}{\square} \times \dfrac{1}{\square}$				
4		$\dfrac{1}{\square} \times \dfrac{1}{\square}$				
5		$\dfrac{1}{\square} \times \dfrac{1}{\square}$				

MY TOTAL POINTS

RECORDING SHEET
Less Is More (Level 1)

> Record your fractions and products and your partner's products.
> Optional: Use the grid paper on page 61 to multiply.

BLOCK 6

ROUND	NUMBERS ROLLED	MULTIPLY THE FRACTIONS	MY PRODUCT	MY PARTNER'S PRODUCT	COMPARE THE FRACTIONS USING >, <, OR =	MY POINTS
1		$\dfrac{1}{\square} \times \dfrac{1}{\square}$				
2		$\dfrac{1}{\square} \times \dfrac{1}{\square}$				
3		$\dfrac{1}{\square} \times \dfrac{1}{\square}$				
4		$\dfrac{1}{\square} \times \dfrac{1}{\square}$				
5		$\dfrac{1}{\square} \times \dfrac{1}{\square}$				

MY TOTAL POINTS

> **Optional:** Use this space to multiply.

> **Answer this question.**

You rolled a 2, 4, and 6. Which numbers would you keep?

_____

> **Explain your reasoning.**

I would keep the numbers _____

and _____ because _____

_____

_____

_____

_____

SCORE ⓪ ① ②

TOPIC 2

CAREER EXPLORATION

> **Particle physicists study the smallest objects in the universe.**

How would a particle physicist use unit fractions to measure small objects?

TOPIC 1

LESSON 5
PROBLEM SOLVING

Solve Compare Problems With Fractions

> WORKED EXAMPLE

Read It! Read and identify the problem.

ASTRONAUT

Lin weighs 90 pounds on Earth. Lin's weight on the Moon is $\frac{1}{6}$ her weight on Earth. How many fewer pounds does she weigh on the Moon?

PROBLEM TYPE _____

Show It! Represent the problem.

90 lb

Earth

d

Moon

Solve It! Solve the problem.

$$\frac{1}{6} \times 90 = \frac{90}{6}$$

$$90 \div 6 = 15$$

$$d = 5 \times 15$$

$$= 75 \text{ lb}$$

Check It! Check your work.

> TRY IT

1

Read It! Read and identify the problem.

ROBOTICS ENGINEER

Curiosity, a Mars rover, is 10 feet long. The length of Sojourner, another rover, is $\frac{1}{5}$ the length of Curiosity. How many feet longer is Curiosity than Sojourner?

PROBLEM TYPE _____

Show It! Represent the problem.

Solve It! Solve the problem.

Check It! Check your work.

> PRACTICE

2

Read It! Read and identify the problem.

FOOD SCIENTIST

Alan freeze-dries food for space travel. A bag of cherries weighs 60 ounces. A bag of peas weighs $\frac{1}{10}$ as many ounces. How many ounces do the two bags weigh together?

PROBLEM TYPE _____

Show It! Represent the problem.

Solve It! Solve the problem.

Check It! Check your work.

How can I use a bar model to represent a compare problem that involves fractions?

3

COMMUNICATIONS ENGINEER

Gia sent two radio signals from Earth to Mars. Signal A traveled to Mars in 56 minutes. Signal B took $\frac{1}{4}$ as long. How many more minutes did Signal A take?

PROBLEM TYPE _____

4

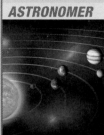

ASTRONOMER

In a scale model, Earth weighs 20 ounces. The weight of Mars is $\frac{1}{10}$ the weight of Earth. How many fewer ounces is the weight of Mars than the weight of Earth in the model?

PROBLEM TYPE _____

EXIT Ticket

BLOCK 6

> **Solve this problem.**

Six men are aboard the International Space Station. There are $\frac{1}{3}$ as many women as men aboard. How many people in all are aboard the International Space Station?

PROBLEM TYPE _____

TOPIC 3

TOPIC 2

TOPIC 1

SCORE ⓪ ① ②

BLOCK 6

LESSON 1
Number Strings

> Multiply each expression mentally.

$5 \times 7 \times 2 \times \frac{1}{7} \times 2 =$ _____

$3 \times 2 \times 3 \times \frac{1}{2} \times 1 =$ _____

$6 \times 5 \times \frac{1}{6} \times 8 \times 3 =$ _____

> Pick one of the expressions and explain how you solved it.

I solved _____

by _____

_____

_____

LESSON 2
Brain Teaser

> Solve this riddle.

• Adam's age is $\frac{1}{2}$ of Bella's age.

• Bella's age is $\frac{2}{3}$ of Chris's age.

• Chris's age is $\frac{1}{3}$ of 36.

How old are the three children?

Adam _____ Bella _____ Chris _____

> How did you begin working on this riddle?

I began working by _____

_____

_____

LESSON 3
Make an Estimate

> Circle the expressions whose products are less than both factors.

$\frac{4}{3} \times \frac{6}{11}$ $\frac{5}{8} \times \frac{8}{9}$

$\frac{2}{5} \times \frac{6}{7}$ $\frac{15}{16} \times \frac{5}{12}$

$\frac{4}{9} \times \frac{3}{2}$ $\frac{7}{10} \times \frac{3}{5}$

> How do you know which products are less than both factors?

I know which products are less

than both factors because _____

_____

_____

LESSON 4

Find the Pattern

> Write another expression in the circle using the rule.

$\frac{2}{3} \times \frac{1}{4}$

$6 \times \frac{2}{3}$
$\frac{1}{3}$ of 12
$\frac{4}{2}$ of $\frac{20}{10}$

$\frac{3}{4} \times \frac{4}{3}$

$\frac{2}{3}$ of 12

> Write the rule for numbers inside the circle.

The numbers inside the circle must

be _____

_____

_____

LESSON 5

Which Does Not Belong?

> Circle the number that does not belong.

$2\frac{1}{2}$ $\frac{5}{2}$ $\frac{10}{4}$ $\frac{5}{4}$ $2\frac{2}{4}$

> How do you know which number does not belong?

_____ does not belong because

_____

_____

_____

> In this Topic, you learned to multiply fractions.

How would I find a product of mixed numbers like $1\frac{1}{2} \times 2\frac{1}{4}$?

Rename each mixed number as a fraction and multiply.

$1\frac{1}{2} \times 2\frac{1}{4}$

$\frac{3}{2} \times \frac{9}{4} = \frac{27}{8}$

$\frac{27}{8} = \frac{24}{8} + \frac{3}{8}$

$\frac{27}{8} = 3\frac{3}{8}$

LESSON 1
CONCEPT

Multiply Fractions and Whole Numbers

> WORKED EXAMPLE   > TRY IT   > PRACTICE

STEP 1 Rename the fraction.

$$27 \times \frac{5}{6}$$

$$\underline{(27} \times \underline{5)} \times \frac{1}{6}$$

STEP 2 Multiply the whole numbers.

$$27 \times \frac{5}{6}$$

$$\underline{(27} \times \underline{5)} \times \frac{1}{6}$$

20 + 7

(20 × 5) + (7 × 5)

100 + 35 = 135

$$135 \times \frac{1}{6}$$

STEP 3 Multiply the whole number by the unit fraction.

$$135 \times \frac{1}{6} = \frac{135}{6}$$

STEP 4 Rename and simplify the fraction.

$$
\begin{array}{r}
2 \\
20 \quad 22\ R3 \\
6)\overline{135} \\
-120 \\
\hline
15 \\
-12 \\
\hline
3
\end{array}
$$

$$\frac{135}{6} = 22\frac{3}{6} \text{ or } 22\frac{1}{2}$$

$$27 \times \frac{5}{6} = \underline{22\frac{1}{2}}$$

1

STEP 1 Rename the fraction.

$$\frac{2}{5} \times 12$$

$$\underline{\quad\quad} \times \underline{\quad\quad} \times \underline{\quad\quad}$$

STEP 2 Multiply the whole numbers.

STEP 3 Multiply the whole number by the unit fraction.

STEP 4 Rename and simplify the fraction.

$$\frac{2}{5} \times 12 = \underline{\quad\quad}$$

2

STEP 1 Rename the fraction.

$$12 \times \frac{3}{4}$$

$$\underline{\quad\quad} \times \underline{\quad\quad} \times \underline{\quad\quad}$$

STEP 2 Multiply the whole numbers.

STEP 3 Multiply the whole number by the unit fraction.

STEP 4 Rename and simplify the fraction.

$$12 \times \frac{3}{4} = \underline{\quad\quad}$$

simplest form *(n)* when the only whole number that divides both the numerator and denominator of a fraction evenly is 1

3

$$\frac{2}{3} \times 9$$

$\bigwedge$

_____ × _____ × _____

$$\frac{2}{3} \times 9 = \underline{\hspace{1cm}}$$

4

$$3 \times \frac{6}{5}$$

$\bigwedge$

_____ × _____ × _____

$$3 \times \frac{6}{5} = \underline{\hspace{1cm}}$$

5

$$8 \times \frac{4}{5}$$

$\bigwedge$

_____ × _____ × _____

$$8 \times \frac{4}{5} = \underline{\hspace{1cm}}$$

6

$$\frac{5}{6} \times 15$$

$\bigwedge$

_____ × _____ × _____

$$\frac{5}{6} \times 15 = \underline{\hspace{1cm}}$$

EXIT Ticket

BLOCK **6**

TOPIC 3

TOPIC 2

TOPIC 1

> **Find the product.**

$$6 \times \frac{3}{10}$$

$\bigwedge$

_____ × _____ × _____

$$6 \times \frac{3}{10} = \underline{\hspace{1cm}}$$

> **How do you know your answer is in simplest form?**

I know my answer is in simplest

form because _____

_____

_____

_____

_____

SCORE ⓪ ① ②

> WORKED EXAMPLE

> TRY IT

> PRACTICE

BLOCK 6

STEP 1 **Estimate the product.**

$$\frac{2}{5} \times \frac{3}{4}$$

Estimate: ___$< \frac{2}{5}$___

STEP 2 **Multiply the fractions.**

$$\frac{2}{5} \times \frac{3}{4} = \frac{6}{20}$$

Rule: The numerator is the product of the numerators. The denominator is the product of the denominators.

STEP 3 **Simplify the product.**

$$\frac{6}{20} \div \frac{2}{2} = \frac{3}{10}$$

$$\frac{2}{5} \times \frac{3}{4} = \frac{3}{10}$$

STEP 4 **Compare the product to the estimate.**

Is your answer reasonable? ___yes___

STEP 1 **Estimate the product.**

$$\frac{3}{2} \times \frac{5}{9}$$

Estimate: _____

STEP 2 **Multiply the fractions.**

STEP 3 **Simplify the product.**

$$\frac{3}{2} \times \frac{5}{9} = \rule{1.5cm}{0.15mm}$$

STEP 4 **Compare the product to the estimate.**

Is your answer reasonable? _____

STEP 1 **Estimate the product.**

$$\frac{2}{3} \times \frac{2}{3}$$

Estimate: _____

STEP 2 **Multiply the fractions.**

STEP 3 **Simplify the product.**

$$\frac{2}{3} \times \frac{2}{3} = \rule{1.5cm}{0.15mm}$$

STEP 4 **Compare the product to the estimate.**

Is your answer reasonable? _____

common denominator *(n)* the denominator of two or more fractions that have the same denominator

3

$$\frac{2}{3} \times \frac{5}{8}$$

Estimate: _____

Is your answer reasonable? _____

4

$$\frac{3}{4} \times \frac{4}{3}$$

Estimate: _____

Is your answer reasonable? _____

5

$$\frac{7}{10} \times \frac{3}{10}$$

Estimate: _____

Is your answer reasonable? _____

6

$$\frac{3}{10} \times \frac{2}{3}$$

Estimate: _____

Is your answer reasonable? _____

7

$$\frac{2}{3} \times \frac{7}{5}$$

Estimate: _____

Is your answer reasonable? _____

8

$$\frac{2}{10} \times \frac{3}{10}$$

Estimate: _____

Is your answer reasonable? _____

EXIT Ticket

BLOCK **6**

TOPIC 3

> **Find the product.**

$$\frac{4}{5} \times \frac{2}{6}$$

Estimate: _____

Is your answer reasonable? _____

TOPIC 2

> **How do you know whether the product will be greater or less than one of the factors?**

The product will be less than both factors if _____

_____

The product will be greater than one factor if _____

_____

TOPIC 1

SCORE ⓪ ① ②

BLOCK 6

When I am not sure which is the lesser fraction, I rename both fractions with a common denominator.

RULES
Less Is More (Level 2)

What You Need
- *mSpace* pages 70–73
- number cube (green, 1–6)

What to Know
- If a player rolls three of the same number, roll again.
- Partners record their products and their partner's products.

How to Win
- The player with the lesser product scores one point.
- The player with the most points after five rounds wins.

> HOW TO PLAY

STEP 1 Roll the number cube four times.

Player A   Player B

 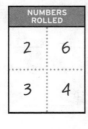

NUMBERS ROLLED	
5	1
4	2

NUMBERS ROLLED	
2	6
3	4

STEP 2 Create two fractions less than 1.

Player A

RECORD THE FRACTIONS

$$\frac{2}{5} \times \frac{1}{4} = \frac{2}{20}$$

Player B

RECORD THE FRACTIONS

$$\frac{3}{4} \times \frac{2}{6} = \frac{6}{24}$$

STEP 3 Record the product of the two fractions.

Player A

MY PRODUCT

$$\frac{2}{20} \div \frac{2}{2} = \frac{1}{10}$$

Player B

MY PRODUCT

$$\frac{6}{24} \div \frac{6}{6} = \frac{1}{4}$$

STEP 4 Write an inequality to compare your product with your partner's product.

Player A

COMPARE THE FRACTIONS USING >, <, OR =	MY POINTS
$\frac{1}{10} < \frac{1}{4}$	1

Player B

COMPARE THE FRACTIONS USING >, <, OR =	MY POINTS
$\frac{1}{4} > \frac{1}{10}$	0

RECORDING SHEET

Less Is More (Level 2)

› Record your products, your partner's products, and the inequalities.
Optional: Use the grid paper on page 73 to record calculations.

ROUND	NUMBERS ROLLED	RECORD THE FRACTIONS	MY PRODUCT	MY PARTNER'S PRODUCT	COMPARE THE FRACTIONS USING >, <, OR =	MY POINTS
1						
2						
3						
4						
5						

MY TOTAL POINTS

RECORDING SHEET
Less Is More (Level 2)

› Record your products, your partner's products, and the inequalities.
Optional: Use the grid paper on page 73 to record calculations.

BLOCK 6

ROUND	NUMBERS ROLLED	RECORD THE FRACTIONS	MY PRODUCT	MY PARTNER'S PRODUCT	COMPARE THE FRACTIONS USING >, <, OR =	MY POINTS
1						
2						
3						
4						
5						

MY TOTAL POINTS

> **Optional: Use this space to record calculations.**

> **Answer this question.**

If you rolled these numbers, what fractions would you create?

> **Explain your reasoning.**

I would create _____ and

_____ because _____

_____

_____

SCORE ⓪ ① ②

CAREER EXPLORATION

> **Astronauts use precise calculations in their experiments.**

How might astronauts measure plant growth in space using fractions?

Multiply Fractions Greater Than 1

> WORKED EXAMPLE   > TRY IT   > PRACTICE

STEP 1 Rename the mixed number as a sum.

$$3 \times 2\frac{4}{5}$$

Rename: $3 \times \left(2 + \frac{4}{5}\right)$

STEP 2 Apply the Distributive Property.

$$3 \times \left(2 + \frac{4}{5}\right)$$
$$(3 \times 2) + \left(3 \times \frac{4}{5}\right)$$
$$6 + \frac{12}{5}$$
$$\frac{12}{5} = \frac{10}{5} + \frac{2}{5}$$
$$= 2\frac{2}{5}$$
$$6 + 2\frac{2}{5} = 8\frac{2}{5}$$

$$3 \times 2\frac{4}{5} = \underline{\quad 8\frac{2}{5} \quad}$$

STEP 3 Rename the mixed numbers as fractions.

$$2\frac{2}{3} \times 3\frac{1}{2}$$

Rename: $\frac{8}{3} \times \frac{7}{2}$

STEP 4 Multiply the fractions.

$$\frac{8}{3} \times \frac{7}{2} = \frac{56}{6}$$
$$\frac{56}{6} = \frac{54}{6} + \frac{2}{6}$$
$$= 9\frac{2}{6} \text{ or } 9\frac{1}{3}$$

$$2\frac{2}{3} \times 3\frac{1}{2} = \underline{\quad 9\frac{1}{3} \quad}$$

1

STEP 1 Rename the mixed number as a sum.

$$4 \times 1\frac{3}{4}$$

Rename:

STEP 2 Apply the Distributive Property.

$$4 \times 1\frac{3}{4} = \underline{\hspace{2cm}}$$

STEP 3 Rename the mixed numbers as fractions.

$$3\frac{2}{3} \times 2\frac{1}{3}$$

Rename:

STEP 4 Multiply the fractions.

$$3\frac{2}{3} \times 2\frac{1}{3} = \underline{\hspace{2cm}}$$

2

STEP 1 Rename the mixed number as a sum.

$$3\frac{1}{8} \times 2$$

Rename:

STEP 2 Apply the Distributive Property.

$$3\frac{1}{8} \times 2 = \underline{\hspace{2cm}}$$

STEP 3 Rename the mixed numbers as fractions.

$$2\frac{1}{2} \times 3\frac{3}{5}$$

Rename:

STEP 4 Multiply the fractions.

$$2\frac{1}{2} \times 3\frac{3}{5} = \underline{\hspace{2cm}}$$

Distributive Property (n) Multiplying a sum by a number is the same as adding the partial products.

3

$$1\frac{3}{8} \times 7$$

4

$$1\frac{2}{3} \times 1\frac{1}{2}$$

5

$$10 \times 2\frac{3}{10}$$

6

$$5 \times 3\frac{3}{4}$$

7

$$3\frac{3}{4} \times 2\frac{2}{3}$$

8

$$2\frac{1}{8} \times 1\frac{1}{4}$$

EXIT Ticket

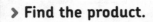

BLOCK 6

> **Find the product.**

$$5 \times 2\frac{2}{3}$$

TOPIC 3

TOPIC 2

> **How did you use the Distributive Property to find the product?**

I used the Distributive Property

by _____

_____

_____

_____

_____

TOPIC 1

SCORE ⓪ ① ②

Strategies for Multiplying Fractions 75

LESSON 5
PROBLEM SOLVING

Solve Multi-Step Problems With Fractions

Read It! Read and identify the problem.

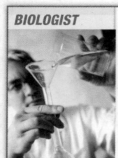

BIOLOGIST

Don used $\frac{1}{3}$ of the water in a full $3\frac{3}{4}$ gallon jug for a water recycling experiment. How many gallons of water were left in the jug?

PROBLEM TYPE _____

Show It! Represent the problem.

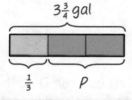

$3\frac{3}{4}$ gal

$\frac{1}{3}$ p

Solve It! Solve the problem.

$3\frac{3}{4} = \frac{12}{4} + \frac{3}{4}$ $p = \frac{2}{3} \times 3\frac{3}{4}$

$\quad = \frac{15}{4}$ $\frac{2}{3} \times \frac{15}{4} = \frac{30}{12}$

$\qquad\qquad\qquad \frac{30}{12} \div \frac{6}{6} = \frac{5}{2}$

$\qquad\qquad p = 2\frac{1}{2}$ gal

Check It! Check your work.

1

Read It! Read and identify the problem.

EQUIPMENT ENGINEER

A camera weighs $2\frac{1}{5}$ pounds on Earth. Objects weigh $\frac{3}{8}$ as much on Mars as on Earth. How many more pounds does the camera weigh on Earth than on Mars?

PROBLEM TYPE _____

Show It! Represent the problem.

Solve It! Solve the problem.

Check It! Check your work.

2

Read It! Read and identify the problem.

ASTRONOMER

A light year is the distance light travels in 1 year. A parsec is a unit of measurement equal to $3\frac{1}{4}$ light years. How many light years are equal to 5 parsecs?

PROBLEM TYPE _____

Show It! Represent the problem.

Solve It! Solve the problem.

Check It! Check your work.

In my bar model, I'll let the bar with 1 unit represent the lesser weight.

3

GEOLOGIST

A Mars rover collects rock samples. It traveled $1\frac{2}{3}$ feet today. By the end of its mission, it will travel $3\frac{1}{2}$ times this distance. How many more feet will the rover travel?

PROBLEM TYPE _____

4

PLANETARY SCIENTIST

A Mars year is $1\frac{8}{9}$ times as long as an Earth year. If a mission lasts $1\frac{1}{2}$ Earth years, then how many Mars years does the mission last?

PROBLEM TYPE _____

EXIT Ticket

> **Solve this problem.**

Objects on Jupiter weigh $2\frac{1}{3}$ times as much as they do on Earth. A battery weighs 3 pounds on Earth. How many more pounds will it weigh on Jupiter?

PROBLEM TYPE _____

BLOCK **6**

TOPIC 3

TOPIC 2

TOPIC 1

SCORE ⓪ ① ②

BLOCK 6

LESSON 1

Build It

> Use only these numbers to build division equations.

 2 3 4 6 12 13 18

- _____
- _____
- _____
- _____

> What number or numbers didn't you use? Why?

I didn't use _____ because

_____

_____

LESSON 2

Brain Teaser

> Solve this riddle.

- When you divide me by $\frac{1}{2}$ the quotient is 12.
- When you divide me by $\frac{1}{3}$ the quotient is 18.
- When you divide me by $\frac{1}{4}$ the quotient is 24.

What number am I? _____

> How did you begin solving this riddle?

I began solving this riddle by

_____

_____

_____

LESSON 3

Missing Numbers

> Fill in the missing numbers.

$$\frac{\Box}{2} \div \frac{2}{\Box} = 10$$

> What was your first step in solving the problem?

My first step in solving the problem

was _____

_____

_____

LESSON 4

Make an Estimate

> For each pair of division expressions, choose the one that you think will result in the lesser quotient and circle it.

$$3 \div \frac{1}{2} \text{ or } 3 \div \frac{1}{4}$$

$$6 \div \frac{1}{12} \text{ or } 6 \div \frac{1}{6}$$

$$5 \div \frac{1}{4} \text{ or } 5 \div \frac{1}{8}$$

> Choose one of the pairs. How do you know which quotient is lesser?

I know that _____ has the

lesser quotient because _____

_____

_____

LESSON 5

Who's Right?

> Fill in the missing number in this pattern.

$$\frac{3}{2}, \frac{9}{4}, \frac{27}{8}, \boxed{}$$

- Raj says the missing number is $\frac{45}{24}$.
- Liz thinks it's $\frac{81}{16}$.

Who's right? _____

> Do you agree with Raj or Liz? Explain your reasoning.

I agree with _____ because

_____

_____

_____

> In this Topic, you learned to divide fractions.

How do I divide fractions like $1\frac{1}{4} \div \frac{3}{8}$?

I write the division as a fraction and then simplify.

$$\frac{5}{4} \div \frac{3}{8}$$

$$\frac{10}{8} \div \frac{3}{8}$$

$$10 \div 3 = \frac{10}{3}$$

$$1\frac{1}{4} \div \frac{3}{8} = 3\frac{1}{3}$$

LESSON 1
CONCEPT

Use Models to Divide

> WORKED EXAMPLE

> TRY IT

> PRACTICE

WORKED EXAMPLE

STEP 1 Represent the problem with fraction shapes.

$$1\frac{3}{4} \div \frac{1}{4}$$

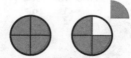

STEP 2 Take out equal groups.

STEP 3 Write the division equation.

$$1\frac{3}{4} \div \frac{1}{4} = \underline{\ 7\ }$$

TRY IT

1

STEP 1 Represent the problem with fraction shapes.

$$2 \div \frac{2}{3}$$

STEP 2 Take out equal groups.

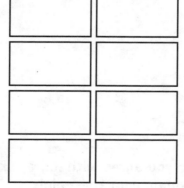

STEP 3 Write the division equation.

$$2 \div \frac{2}{3} = \underline{\hspace{1cm}}$$

PRACTICE

2

STEP 1 Represent the problem with fraction shapes.

$$4 \div \frac{4}{5}$$

STEP 2 Take out equal groups.

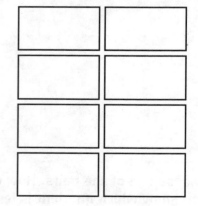

STEP 3 Write the division equation.

$$4 \div \frac{4}{5} = \underline{\hspace{1cm}}$$

3

$$2 \div \frac{1}{4}$$

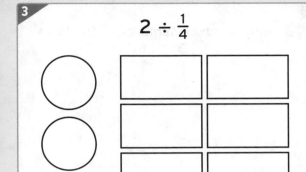

$$2 \div \frac{1}{4} = \underline{\hspace{2cm}}$$

4

$$3\frac{3}{4} \div \frac{3}{4}$$

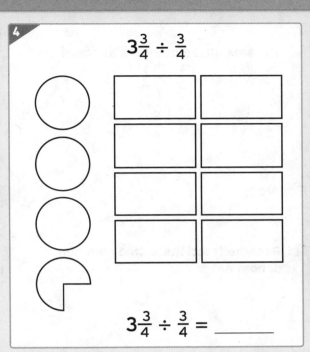

$$3\frac{3}{4} \div \frac{3}{4} = \underline{\hspace{2cm}}$$

5

$$2\frac{2}{8} \div \frac{3}{8}$$

$$2\frac{2}{8} \div \frac{3}{8} = \underline{\hspace{2cm}}$$

6

$$2\frac{3}{6} \div \frac{3}{6}$$

$$2\frac{3}{6} \div \frac{3}{6} = \underline{\hspace{2cm}}$$

EXIT Ticket

BLOCK
6
TOPIC 3

> **Find the quotient.**

$$1\frac{4}{8} \div \frac{3}{8}$$

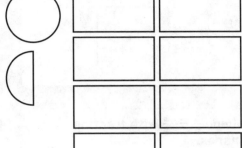

$$1\frac{4}{8} \div \frac{3}{8} = \underline{\hspace{2cm}}$$

TOPIC 2

> **Explain how you used fraction shapes to find the quotient.**

I used fraction shapes to find the quotient by _____

_____

_____

_____

_____

_____

TOPIC 1

SCORE ⓪ ① ②

Strategies for Dividing Fractions **81**

LESSON 2
CONCEPT

Divide by Unit Fractions

STEP 1 Divide $\frac{9}{4} \div \frac{3}{4}$ with fraction shapes.

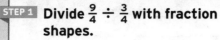

STEP 2 Divide $\frac{6}{5} \div \frac{3}{5}$ with fraction shapes.

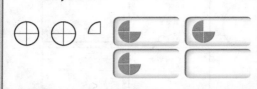

STEP 3 Divide $\frac{10}{8} \div \frac{2}{8}$ with fraction shapes.

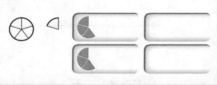

STEP 4 Identify the rule.

$$\frac{9}{4} \div \frac{3}{4} = 3$$
$$\frac{6}{5} \div \frac{3}{5} = 2$$
$$\frac{10}{8} \div \frac{2}{8} = 5$$

Rule: To divide fractions with common denominators, I ___divide the numerators___.

1

STEP 1 Rename mixed numbers as fractions.

$$1\frac{1}{3} \div \frac{1}{4}$$

Rename:

STEP 2 Rename fractions with a common denominator.

STEP 3 Divide the fractions.

STEP 4 Simplify the quotient.

$$1\frac{1}{3} \div \frac{1}{4} = \underline{\qquad}$$

2

STEP 1 Rename mixed numbers as fractions.

$$1\frac{3}{8} \div \frac{1}{4}$$

Rename:

STEP 2 Rename fractions with a common denominator.

STEP 3 Divide the fractions.

STEP 4 Simplify the quotient.

$$1\frac{3}{8} \div \frac{1}{4} = \underline{\qquad}$$

dividend (n) the number that is divided into equal parts or groups; the number you divide

> PRACTICE

3	4
$\frac{4}{5} \div \frac{1}{10}$	$1\frac{2}{3} \div \frac{1}{6}$

5	6
$\frac{1}{3} \div \frac{1}{5}$	$2\frac{2}{3} \div \frac{1}{2}$

7	8
$\frac{8}{10} \div \frac{1}{3}$	$1\frac{4}{8} \div \frac{1}{3}$

BLOCK
6

TOPIC 3

> **Find the quotient.**

$$3\frac{1}{6} \div \frac{1}{3}$$

> **Why can we divide the numerators when dividing fractions?**

We can divide numerators

because _____

_____

_____

_____

_____

_____

SCORE ⓪ ① ②

BLOCK 6

> WORKED EXAMPLE

STEP 1 Rename mixed numbers as fractions.

$$2\frac{5}{6} \div \frac{3}{8}$$

Rename: $\frac{17}{6} \div \frac{3}{8}$

STEP 2 Rename fractions with a common denominator.

$$\frac{17}{6} \times \frac{4}{4} = \frac{68}{24}$$

$$\frac{3}{8} \times \frac{3}{3} = \frac{9}{24}$$

$$\frac{68}{24} \div \frac{9}{24}$$

STEP 3 Divide the fractions.

$$68 \div 9 = \frac{68}{9}$$

$$\frac{68}{9} = \frac{63}{9} + \frac{5}{9}$$

$$= 7\frac{5}{9}$$

STEP 4 Simplify the quotient.

$$2\frac{5}{6} \div \frac{3}{8} = \underline{7\frac{5}{9}}$$

> TRY IT

1

STEP 1 Rename mixed numbers as fractions.

$$\frac{3}{4} \div 1\frac{1}{5}$$

Rename:

STEP 2 Rename fractions with a common denominator.

STEP 3 Divide the fractions.

STEP 4 Simplify the quotient.

$$\frac{3}{4} \div 1\frac{1}{5} = \underline{\hspace{1cm}}$$

> PRACTICE

2

STEP 1 Rename mixed numbers as fractions.

$$1\frac{1}{3} \div \frac{3}{10}$$

Rename:

STEP 2 Rename fractions with a common denominator.

STEP 3 Divide the fractions.

STEP 4 Simplify the quotient.

$$1\frac{1}{3} \div \frac{3}{10} = \underline{\hspace{1cm}}$$

equivalent fractions *(n)* two or more fractions that name the same part of a whole

> PRACTICE

3

$$2\frac{3}{4} \div 1\frac{1}{8}$$

4

$$2\frac{5}{8} \div \frac{1}{3}$$

5

$$1\frac{2}{7} \div \frac{4}{5}$$

6

$$\frac{2}{3} \div 1\frac{6}{30}$$

BLOCK
6
TOPIC 3
TOPIC 2
TOPIC 1

> **Find the quotient.**

$$\frac{8}{10} \div 1\frac{4}{5}$$

> **How do you know when a quotient will be less than 1?**

A quotient will be less than 1

when _____

_____

_____

_____

_____

_____

_____

SCORE ⓪ ① ②

Use Strategies to Divide Fractions

Before I place my numbers, I like to write out all possible equations so I can create the least possible quotient.

RULES

Less Is More (Level 3)

What You Need
- *mSpace* pages 86–89
- number cube (green, 1–6)

What to Know
- If a player rolls three of the same number, roll again.
- Partners record their quotients and their partner's quotients.

How to Win
- The player with the lesser quotient scores one point.
- The player with the most points after five rounds wins.

> HOW TO PLAY

STEP 1 Roll the number cube three times.

Player A

Player B

STEP 2 Create two fractions less than 1.

Player A

DIVIDE THE FRACTIONS
$\dfrac{4}{5} \div \dfrac{1}{3} =$

Player B

DIVIDE THE FRACTIONS
$\dfrac{2}{3} \div \dfrac{1}{6} =$

STEP 3 Divide the fractions. Record your quotient and your partner's quotient.

Player A

DIVIDE THE FRACTIONS	MY QUOTIENT
$\dfrac{4}{5} \div \dfrac{1}{3} = \dfrac{12}{15} \div \dfrac{5}{15}$	$2\dfrac{2}{5}$

Player B

DIVIDE THE FRACTIONS	MY QUOTIENT
$\dfrac{2}{3} \div \dfrac{1}{6} = \dfrac{4}{6} \div \dfrac{1}{6}$	4

STEP 4 Compare your quotient with your partner's quotient.

Player A

COMPARE THE FRACTIONS USING >, <, OR =	MY POINTS
$2\dfrac{2}{5} < 4$	1

Player B

COMPARE THE FRACTIONS USING >, <, OR =	MY POINTS
$4 > 2\dfrac{2}{5}$	0

RECORDING SHEET

Less Is More (Level 3)

> Record your quotients and your partner's quotients.
> Optional: Use the space on page 89 to write division equations.

ROUND	NUMBERS ROLLED	DIVIDE THE FRACTIONS	MY QUOTIENT	MY PARTNER'S QUOTIENT	COMPARE THE FRACTIONS USING >, <, OR =	MY POINTS
1		$\dfrac{\square}{\square} \div \dfrac{1}{\square} =$				
2		$\dfrac{\square}{\square} \div \dfrac{1}{\square} =$				
3		$\dfrac{\square}{\square} \div \dfrac{1}{\square} =$				
4		$\dfrac{\square}{\square} \div \dfrac{1}{\square} =$				
5		$\dfrac{\square}{\square} \div \dfrac{1}{\square} =$				

MY TOTAL POINTS

> Record your quotients and your partner's quotients.
Optional: Use the space on page 89 to write division equations.

BLOCK 6

ROUND	NUMBERS ROLLED		DIVIDE THE FRACTIONS	MY QUOTIENT	MY PARTNER'S QUOTIENT	COMPARE THE FRACTIONS USING >, <, OR =	MY POINTS
1			$\dfrac{\square}{\square} \div \dfrac{1}{\square} =$				
2			$\dfrac{\square}{\square} \div \dfrac{1}{\square} =$				
3			$\dfrac{\square}{\square} \div \dfrac{1}{\square} =$				
4			$\dfrac{\square}{\square} \div \dfrac{1}{\square} =$				
5			$\dfrac{\square}{\square} \div \dfrac{1}{\square} =$				
							MY TOTAL POINTS

> Optional: Use this space to write division equations.

EXIT
Ticket

BLOCK
6

TOPIC 3

TOPIC 2

TOPIC 1

> **Answer this question.**
If you rolled these numbers, what fractions would you create?

$$\frac{\Box}{\Box} \div \frac{1}{\Box}$$

> **Can you arrange the numbers another way and still get the same quotient? If so, how?**

I could arrange the numbers

like this $\dfrac{\Box}{\Box} \div \dfrac{1}{\Box}$ and get the

same quotient.

SCORE ⓪ ① ②

CAREER EXPLORATION

> **Dieticians select foods to create well-balanced meals.**

How might dieticians use fractions to plan meals for a school cafeteria?

LESSON 5
PROBLEM SOLVING

Identify Patterns With Fractions

> WORKED EXAMPLE   > TRY IT   > PRACTICE

BLOCK 6

STEP 1 Find the rule using multiplication.

INPUT	EQUATIONS	OUTPUT
1	$1 \times \frac{1}{2} = \frac{1}{2}$	$\frac{1}{2}$
$\frac{1}{2}$	$\frac{1}{2} \times \frac{1}{2} = \frac{1}{4}$	$\frac{1}{4}$
$\frac{1}{4}$	$\frac{1}{4} \times \frac{1}{2} = \frac{1}{8}$	$\frac{1}{8}$
$\frac{1}{5}$		$\frac{1}{10}$
16		8

Output = Input × $\frac{1}{2}$

Output = $\underline{C}$ × $\frac{1}{2}$ or $\frac{1}{2}C$

STEP 2 Represent the rule with division.

INPUT	EQUATIONS		OUTPUT
1	$1 \times \frac{1}{2} = \frac{1}{2}$	$1 \div 2 = \frac{1}{2}$	$\frac{1}{2}$
$\frac{1}{2}$	$\frac{1}{2} \times \frac{1}{2} = \frac{1}{4}$	$\frac{1}{2} \div 2 = \frac{1}{4}$	$\frac{1}{4}$
$\frac{1}{4}$	$\frac{1}{4} \times \frac{1}{2} = \frac{1}{8}$	$\frac{1}{4} \div 2 = \frac{1}{8}$	$\frac{1}{8}$
$\frac{1}{5}$			$\frac{1}{10}$
16			8

Output = Input ÷ $\underline{2}$

Output = $\underline{C}$ ÷ $\underline{2}$

STEP 3 Apply the rule to complete the table.

INPUT	EQUATIONS		OUTPUT
1	$1 \times \frac{1}{2} = \frac{1}{2}$	$1 \div 2 = \frac{1}{2}$	$\frac{1}{2}$
$\frac{1}{2}$	$\frac{1}{2} \times \frac{1}{2} = \frac{1}{4}$	$\frac{1}{2} \div 2 = \frac{1}{4}$	$\frac{1}{4}$
$\frac{1}{4}$	$\frac{1}{4} \times \frac{1}{2} = \frac{1}{8}$	$\frac{1}{4} \div 2 = \frac{1}{8}$	$\frac{1}{8}$
$\frac{1}{5}$	$\frac{1}{5} \times \frac{1}{2} = \frac{1}{10}$		$\frac{1}{10}$
16		$16 \div 2 = 8$	8

1

STEP 1 Identify the rule.

INPUT	EQUATIONS	OUTPUT
1		$\frac{1}{4}$
2		$\frac{1}{2}$
3		$\frac{3}{4}$
5		
$\frac{1}{10}$		

STEP 2 Write the rule.

Output = _____ × _____

Output = _____ ÷ _____

STEP 3 Apply the rule to complete the table.

2

STEP 1 Identify the rule.

INPUT	EQUATIONS	OUTPUT
1		$\frac{1}{5}$
3		$\frac{3}{5}$
$\frac{1}{2}$		
5		
$\frac{1}{8}$		

STEP 2 Write the rule.

Output = _____ × _____

Output = _____ ÷ _____

STEP 3 Apply the rule to complete the table.

How can understanding the structure of a function table help me identify a pattern involving fractions?

3

STEP 1 Identify the rule.

INPUT	EQUATIONS	OUTPUT
$\frac{1}{2}$		$\frac{7}{2}$
$\frac{1}{5}$		$\frac{7}{5}$
2		
$\frac{4}{7}$		
5		

STEP 2 Write the rule.

Output = _____ × _____

Output = _____ ÷ _____

STEP 3 Apply the rule to complete the table.

4

STEP 1 Identify the rule.

INPUT	EQUATIONS	OUTPUT
1		10
$\frac{1}{6}$		$\frac{10}{6}$
3		
$\frac{2}{3}$		
8		

STEP 2 Write the rule.

Output = _____ × _____

Output = _____ ÷ _____

STEP 3 Apply the rule to complete the table.

BLOCK 6

TOPIC 3

> Complete the function table.

INPUT	EQUATIONS	OUTPUT
1		3
$\frac{1}{2}$		$\frac{3}{2}$
3		
$\frac{1}{6}$		
12		
$\frac{1}{24}$		

TOPIC 2

> Identify the rule and complete the sentence frames.

For every input *n*, the value of

the output is _____ × _____.

Another way I can write the

rule is output = _____ ÷ _____.

If the input is 50, the output

is _____.

TOPIC 1

SCORE ⓪ ① ②

Strategies for Dividing Fractions 91

PERFORMANCE TASK

> **YOUR JOB**
> Mission Planner

> **YOUR TASK**
> Divide floor space on a space station and calculate the areas.

ANCHOR VIDEO CONNECTION

As the Anchor Video shows, every detail of a space mission is carefully planned.

Organize Space Experiments

> **Four teams of scientists are designing experiments to send into space. Your task is to divide a square area of floor on the space station for the experiments. Try to meet the scientists' requests and to give each experiment about the same area.**

A EXPLORE

The square space measures $1\frac{1}{2}$ meters on each side. Draw lines on the diagram to separate the square into four sections, one for each experiment.

SAMPLE PLAN

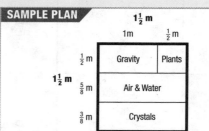

Science Experiments for a Space Station
Plants in Space
Request: We need a square area.
Air & Water Quality
Request: We would like a rectangular area that is as long as possible.
Gravity Experiment
Request: We need a rectangular area that is twice as long as it is wide.
Crystals in Space
Request: We cannot be next to the gravity experiment. Its equipment would affect our results.

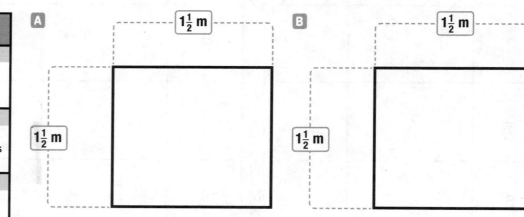

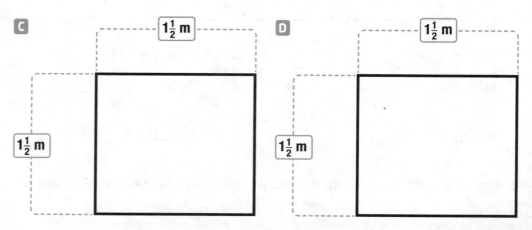

A Drew and labeled four different plans.

Me	0	1	2	3
Partner	0	1	2	3

B Calculated areas for two of the plans.

Me	0	1	2	3
Partner	0	1	2	3

C Answered each question accurately.

Me	0	1	2	3
Partner	0	1	2	3

EXTEND

Change one plan to fill a square that is 3 meters on each side. How much larger does each of the four areas become?

B APPLY

Choose two plans from Part A that you think work best. For each plan, complete the table to find the area for each experiment.

PLAN _____

EXPERIMENT	SIZE (m × m)	CALCULATIONS	AREA (m²)
Plants			
Air & Water			
Gravity			
Crystals			
TOTAL			

PLAN _____

EXPERIMENT	SIZE (m × m)	CALCULATIONS	AREA (m²)
Plants			
Air & Water			
Gravity			
Crystals			
TOTAL			

C ANALYZE

INTERPRET Which of your plans do you think is most fair to the scientists? Explain your choice.

_____

_____

REFLECT Do you think it's possible to meet all of the requests and give each experiment equal area? Explain.

_____

_____

MINDSET SCAN

BLOCK 6

Scan Your Learning Attitudes

Congratulations! You've completed Block 6 of *MATH 180*. For each question, fill in the circle that best describes your mindset. Then complete the sentence frames.

A GETTING FOCUSED

Focusing your attention on a task, such as solving a math problem, is the first step to completing it successfully.

Did you pay attention as the teacher solved BLOCK 6 math problems?

① I let my mind wander and was easily distracted when the teacher solved math problems.

② I tried to pay attention to each problem, but sometimes my mind wandered. I usually did not suggest answers to the teacher's questions.

③ I paid close attention to the solutions, and I carefully thought about the teacher's questions and suggested answers to them.

I (did/did not) pay close attention in class because

_____

_____

_____

B EXPANDING AND DEVELOPING BRAIN CONNECTIONS

New brain pathways and connections allow you to think in new ways and solve new problems.

Did you commit time and effort to the Brain Arcade during BLOCK 6 ?

① I played only a few Brain Arcade games, and I did not worry about my score or performance.

② I played Brain Arcade games when I had spare time, but not always when I needed extra practice.

③ I played Brain Arcade games regularly to improve my math skills.

I spent (little/some/a lot of) time on the Brain Arcade because _____

_____

_____

C PERSISTENCE

When you keep trying new ways to solve difficult problems, you eventually will succeed.

How did you approach difficult BLOCK 6 math problems?

① I did not try to solve math problems that seemed too difficult.

② I tried to solve difficult math problems, but often I gave up when I could not find the solution quickly.

③ I kept trying as much as possible and didn't give up. I reviewed earlier work, and I asked a classmate or teacher to help me understand.

I (never/sometimes/often) gave up on math problems because _____

_____

_____

D KEEPING A POSITIVE MOOD AND MOTIVATION

Learning math can be challenging. Keeping a positive mood can help you succeed.

Did you keep a positive mood as you studied math in BLOCK 6 ?

① I often had negative thoughts about my math skills, and these thoughts affected my studying.

② I struggled to keep a positive mood while studying difficult math concepts.

③ I reminded myself that I was succeeding at math because I was working hard and not giving up.

I (did/did not) keep a positive mood because _____

_____

_____

Score Your Mindset

> Add up all the numbers that you checked (1, 2, or 3.) Then read the feedback in the chart.

 TOTAL SCORE

If your total score was: *You were in the:*

6 or less

Fixed Mindset Zone
You were in the Fixed Mindset Zone this time. Your mindset may have held you back from doing your best.

 **7–10**

Mixed Mindset Zone
You were in the Mixed Mindset Zone this time. You may have used some Growth Mindset thinking, but in other ways you may have held yourself back.

 11 or more

Growth Mindset Zone
You were in the Growth Mindset Zone this time. You used strategies that will help you grow your brain and get smarter.

> **How can you develop a Growth Mindset?**

- Read the statements in the Mindset Scan again.
- Make a plan to help you choose the third statement in each category when you take a scan like this one again. Include specific goals in your plan.
- Review your plan as you study. Try to meet the goals you set for yourself.

Brain Boosting

> **What will you do to help your brain stay in the Growth Mindset Zone?**

I will work to:

☐ Stay focused

☐ Develop brain connections

☐ Be persistent

☐ Keep a positive mood

" Luck has nothing to do with it, because I have spent many, many hours, countless hours, on the court working for my one moment in time, not knowing when it would come. "

Serena Williams, Tennis champion

What will I do?

_____
_____
_____
_____
_____

Who will help me?

_____
_____
_____
_____
_____

When will I do it?

_____
_____
_____
_____
_____

How will this help me to grow?

_____
_____
_____
_____
_____

VOCABULARY

decimal number

decimal point

hundredths

intersection

place value

ten-thousandths

tenths

thousandths

Against the Clock

Do you have what it takes to be an Olympic athlete?

In this Anchor Video, experts use a combination of precise timing and technology to measure the speed of an Olympic champion.

LESSON 4

Which Does Not Belong?

> Circle the number that does not belong.

0.7, $\frac{70}{100}$, 0.07, $\frac{7}{10}$, 0.70

> How could you use a decimal grid to prove your answer?

I can use a decimal grid by _____

_____

_____

LESSON 5

Missing Numbers

> Use each of the five numbers once to create a fraction that is equivalent to a decimal.

0, 3, 4, 5, 7

$$\frac{\square}{\square} = \square.\square\square$$

> How do you know your equation is correct?

I know my equation is correct

because _____

_____

_____

> In this Topic, you learned to name fractions as decimals. You used decimal grids to represent fractions.

Is the fraction $\frac{3}{25}$ equal to the decimal 0.12? How do I know?

Yes! You can rename $\frac{3}{25}$ as $\frac{12}{100}$, and $\frac{12}{100}$ is equal to 0.12.

$$\frac{3 \times 4}{25 \times 4} = \frac{12}{100}$$

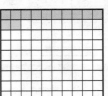

Name Fractions Using Decimal Notation

> WORKED EXAMPLE

> TRY IT

> PRACTICE

BLOCK 7

WORKED EXAMPLE

STEP 1 **Identify tenths.**

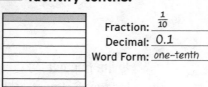

Fraction: $\frac{1}{10}$

Decimal: 0.1

Word Form: one-tenth

STEP 2 **Identify hundredths.**

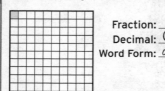

Fraction: $\frac{1}{100}$

Decimal: 0.01

Word Form: one-hundredth

STEP 3 **Name tenths and hundredths.**

Fraction: $\frac{4}{10}$ + $\frac{2}{100}$

$\frac{40}{100}$ + $\frac{2}{100}$ = $\frac{42}{100}$

STEP 4 **Write decimal numbers.**

Decimal: 0.42

Word Form: forty-two hundredths

TRY IT

1

STEP 1 **Identify tenths and hundredths.**

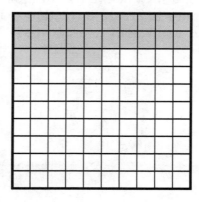

Fraction: _____ + _____

STEP 2 **Add fractions.**

_____ + _____ = _____

STEP 3 **Write the fraction as a decimal.**

Decimal: _____

STEP 4 **Name the decimal in word form.**

Word Form: _____

PRACTICE

2

STEP 1 **Identify tenths and hundredths.**

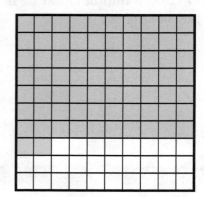

Fraction: _____ + _____

STEP 2 **Add fractions.**

_____ + _____ = _____

STEP 3 **Write the fraction as a decimal.**

Decimal: _____

STEP 4 **Name the decimal in word form.**

Word Form: _____

decimal number *(n)* a number that has a decimal point followed by digits

3

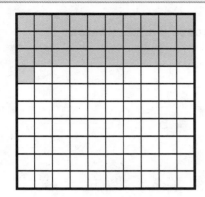

Fraction: _____ + _____

_____ + _____ = _____

Decimal: _____

Word Form: _____

4

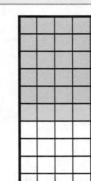

Fraction: _____ + _____

_____ + _____ = _____

Decimal: _____

Word Form: _____

5

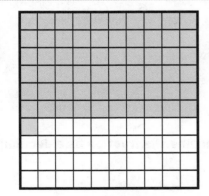

Fraction: _____ + _____

_____ + _____ = _____

Decimal: _____

Word Form: _____

6

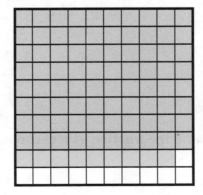

Fraction: _____ + _____

_____ + _____ = _____

Decimal: _____

Word Form: _____

EXIT Ticket

BLOCK 7

> **Solve this problem.**
Name the number as a fraction, as a decimal, and in word form.

TOPIC 3

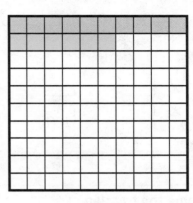

Fraction: _____ + _____

_____ + _____ = _____

Decimal: _____

Word Form: _____

TOPIC 2

The decimal numbers 0.3 and 0.03 have different values. 0.3 is equal to $\frac{3}{10}$ and 0.03 is equal to $\frac{3}{100}$.

TOPIC 1

SCORE ⓪ ① ②

Name Fractions as Decimals

> WORKED EXAMPLE

> TRY IT

> PRACTICE

STEP 1 Choose a denominator.

$$\frac{6}{25} = 0.\underline{\hspace{1cm}}$$

$$\frac{6}{25} \times \frac{\square}{\square} = \frac{\square}{100}$$

STEP 2 Rename the fraction.

$$\frac{6}{25} \times \frac{4}{4} = \frac{24}{100}$$

STEP 3 Rename the fraction as a decimal.

$$\frac{6}{25} = \underline{0.24}$$

1

STEP 1 Choose a denominator.

$$\frac{1}{4} = 0.\underline{\hspace{1cm}}$$

STEP 2 Rename the fraction.

$$\frac{1}{4} \times \frac{\square}{\square} = \frac{\square}{\square}$$

STEP 3 Rename the fraction as a decimal.

$$\frac{1}{4} = \underline{\hspace{1cm}}$$

2

STEP 1 Choose a denominator.

$$\frac{4}{5} = 0.\underline{\hspace{1cm}}$$

STEP 2 Rename the fraction.

$$\frac{4}{5} \times \frac{\square}{\square} = \frac{\square}{\square}$$

STEP 3 Rename the fraction as a decimal.

$$\frac{4}{5} = \underline{\hspace{1cm}}$$

BLOCK 7

decimal point *(n)* a symbol (dot or period) used to separate the whole number part from the fractional part in a decimal number

3

$\frac{1}{2} = 0.$ _____

$\frac{1}{2} \begin{array}{c} \times\ \square \\ \times\ \square \end{array} = \frac{\square}{\square}$

$\frac{1}{2} =$ _____

4

$\frac{3}{25} = 0.$ _____

$\frac{3}{25} \begin{array}{c} \times\ \square \\ \times\ \square \end{array} = \frac{\square}{\square}$

$\frac{3}{25} =$ _____

5

$\frac{12}{50} = 0.$ _____

$\frac{12}{50} \begin{array}{c} \times\ \square \\ \times\ \square \end{array} = \frac{\square}{\square}$

$\frac{12}{50} =$ _____

6

$\frac{9}{20} = 0.$ _____

$\frac{9}{20} \begin{array}{c} \times\ \square \\ \times\ \square \end{array} = \frac{\square}{\square}$

$\frac{9}{20} =$ _____

EXIT Ticket

BLOCK **7**

› **Find the error and fix the math.**

$$\frac{3}{4} = 0.\ \_\_\_$$

$$\frac{3}{4} \times \frac{1}{25} = \frac{3}{100}$$

$$\frac{3}{4} = 0.03$$

TOPIC 3

TOPIC 2

› **Explain the error and how you fixed it.**

The error I found was _____

_____

_____

_____

_____

_____

TOPIC 1

I fixed the error by _____

_____

_____

SCORE ⓪ ① ②

Fraction and Decimal Relationships **101**

LESSON 3
GAME

Develop Reasoning With Decimals

I can win by filling the grid, or by stopping when the grid is almost full.

RULES

Over & Out (Level 1)

What You Need

- *mSpace* pages 102–105
- decahedron (black, 0–9)

What to Know

- Players fill as much of their decimal grids as possible.
- Stop when you think your grid is filled enough to win.
- Once a player has decided to stop, turns cannot be made afterwards.

How to Win

- The first player to fill the decimal grid in 10 turns wins.
- If both players have stopped, the player whose grid is closest to being filled is the winner.
- If a player goes over shading one grid, the other player wins.

> HOW TO PLAY

STEP 1 Roll the decahedron and record that number.

NUMBERS ROLLED	DECIMALS USED
5	

STEP 2 Decide whether the number rolled should be a decimal in the tenths place or the hundredths place.

NUMBERS ROLLED	DECIMALS USED
5	0.5

STEP 3 Shade the decimal in the grid.

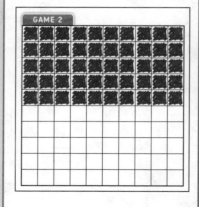

GAME 2

STEP 4 Take turns with your partner.

RECORDING SHEET

Over & Out (Level 1)

> Record the numbers you rolled and shade the grid with the decimals chosen.
> Optional: Use the grid paper on page 105 for calculations.

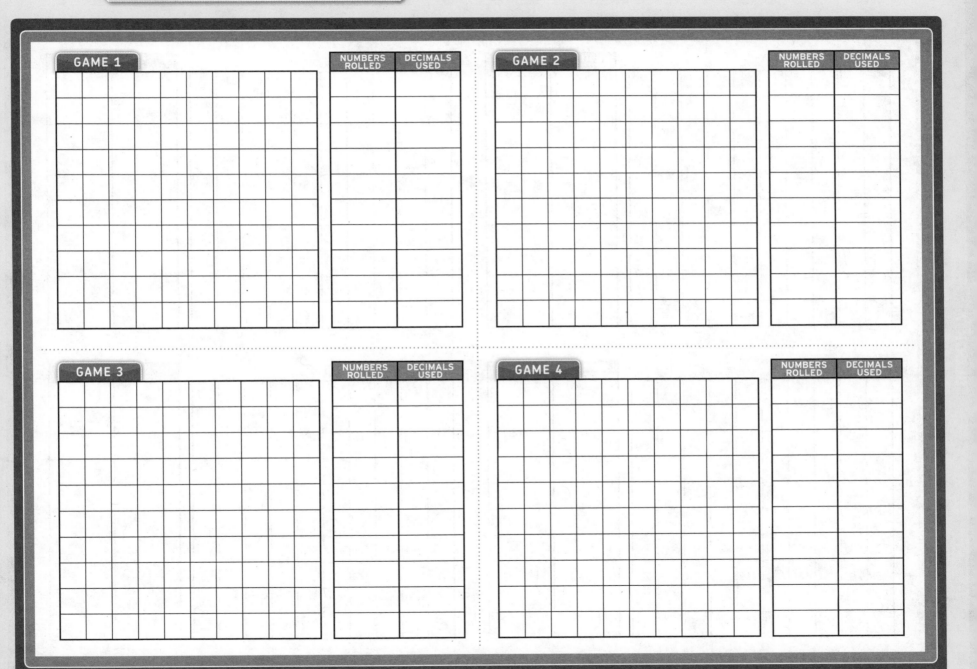

GAME 1

NUMBERS ROLLED	DECIMALS USED

GAME 2

NUMBERS ROLLED	DECIMALS USED

GAME 3

NUMBERS ROLLED	DECIMALS USED

GAME 4

NUMBERS ROLLED	DECIMALS USED

RECORDING SHEET
Over & Out (Level 1)

> Record the numbers you rolled and shade the grid with the decimals chosen. Optional: Use the grid paper on page 105 for calculations.

BLOCK 7

GAME 5

NUMBERS ROLLED	DECIMALS USED

GAME 6

NUMBERS ROLLED	DECIMALS USED

GAME 7

NUMBERS ROLLED	DECIMALS USED

GAME 8

NUMBERS ROLLED	DECIMALS USED

> **Optional: Use this space for calculations.**

> **Answer this question.**

What strategy would you suggest to friends to help them win this game?

The strategy I would tell them is

_____

_____

_____

_____

_____

_____

SCORE ⓪ ① ②

CAREER EXPLORATION

> **Sports officials time track races to hundredths of a second.**

NEW WR
40.82

Why must sports officials know the difference between tenths and hundredths of a second?

TOPIC 3

TOPIC 2

TOPIC 1

BLOCK 7 > TOPIC 1
LESSON 4
CONCEPT

> WORKED EXAMPLE

> TRY IT

> PRACTICE

Express Decimals in More Than One Way

WORKED EXAMPLE

STEP 1 Name the mixed number.

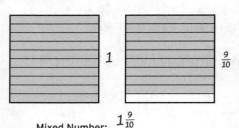

Mixed Number: $1\frac{9}{10}$

STEP 2 Name the decimal.

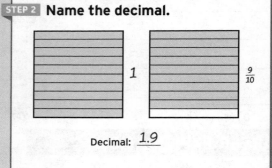

Decimal: 1.9

STEP 3 Name the fraction.

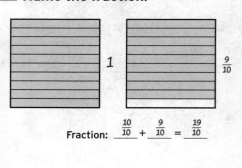

Fraction: $\frac{10}{10} + \frac{9}{10} = \frac{19}{10}$

TRY IT

1

STEP 1 Name the mixed number.

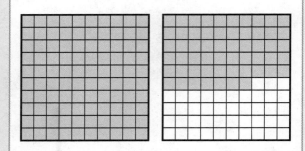

Mixed Number: _____

STEP 2 Name the decimal.

Decimal: _____

STEP 3 Name the fraction.

Fraction: _____ + _____ = _____

PRACTICE

2

STEP 1 Name the mixed number.

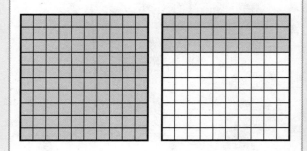

Mixed Number: _____

STEP 2 Name the decimal.

Decimal: _____

STEP 3 Name the fraction.

Fraction: _____ + _____ = _____

> PRACTICE

3

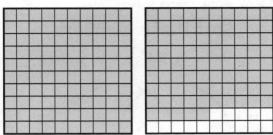

Mixed Number: _____

Decimal: _____

Fraction: _____ + _____ = _____

4

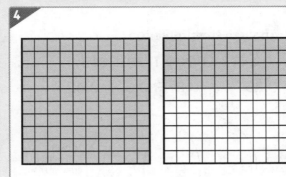

Mixed Number: _____

Decimal: _____

Fraction: _____ + _____ = _____

5

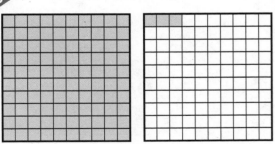

Mixed Number: _____

Decimal: _____

Fraction: _____ + _____ = _____

6

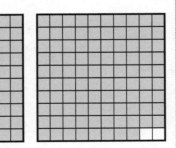

Mixed Number: _____

Decimal: _____

Fraction: _____ + _____ = _____

> **Solve this problem.**

The two decimal grids show a number. Write the number in three different ways.

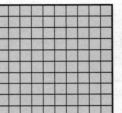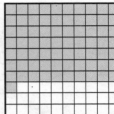

TOPIC **3**

Mixed Number: _____

Decimal: _____

Fraction: _____ + _____ = _____

TOPIC **2**

> **How can you tell when a fraction and a decimal are equivalent?**

A fraction and a decimal are

equivalent when _____

TOPIC **1**

_____

_____

_____

_____

_____

SCORE ⓪ ① ②

> WORKED EXAMPLE

> TRY IT

> PRACTICE

WORKED EXAMPLE

STEP 1 Analyze the problem.

Sort these numbers.

0.13, $\frac{3}{10}$, 0.75, 0.9, $\frac{1}{10}$, $\frac{1}{5}$, 0.4, $\frac{3}{4}$

CIRCLE A Numbers less than $\frac{1}{2} = \frac{50}{100}$

CIRCLE B Numbers greater than $\frac{1}{4} = \frac{25}{100}$

STEP 2 Rename the numbers as hundredths.

$0.13 = \frac{13}{100}$ $0.75 = \frac{75}{100}$ $0.9 = \frac{90}{100}$ $0.4 = \frac{40}{100}$

$\frac{3}{10} = \frac{30}{100}$ $\frac{1}{10} = \frac{10}{100}$ $\frac{1}{5} = \frac{20}{100}$ $\frac{3}{4} = \frac{75}{100}$

STEP 3 Place the numbers in the intersection.

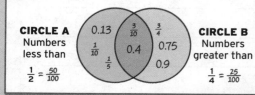

CIRCLE A Numbers less than $\frac{1}{2} = \frac{50}{100}$

CIRCLE B Numbers greater than $\frac{1}{4} = \frac{25}{100}$

STEP 4 Complete the Venn diagram.

CIRCLE A Numbers less than $\frac{1}{2} = \frac{50}{100}$

0.13 $\frac{3}{10}$ $\frac{3}{4}$ $\frac{1}{10}$ 0.4   0.75 $\frac{1}{5}$ 0.9

CIRCLE B Numbers greater than $\frac{1}{4} = \frac{25}{100}$

1

STEP 1 Analyze the problem.

Sort these numbers.

0.25, $\frac{1}{2}$, $\frac{3}{10}$, 0.8, $\frac{4}{5}$, 0.6, $\frac{3}{4}$, 0.42

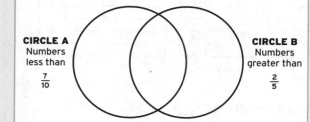

CIRCLE A Numbers less than $\frac{7}{10}$

CIRCLE B Numbers greater than $\frac{2}{5}$

STEP 2 Rename the numbers as hundredths.

STEP 3 Place the numbers in the intersection.

STEP 4 Complete the Venn diagram.

2

STEP 1 Analyze the problem.

Sort these numbers.

$\frac{5}{10}$, 0.65, $\frac{45}{50}$, 0.1, $\frac{7}{10}$, 0.9, $\frac{1}{2}$, 0.55

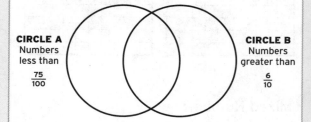

CIRCLE A Numbers less than $\frac{75}{100}$

CIRCLE B Numbers greater than $\frac{6}{10}$

STEP 2 Rename the numbers as hundredths.

STEP 3 Place the numbers in the intersection.

STEP 4 Complete the Venn diagram.

3

Sort these numbers.

$\frac{9}{10}$, 0.85, $\frac{4}{5}$, $\frac{18}{20}$, $\frac{6}{10}$, 0.72, $\frac{1}{2}$, $\frac{20}{25}$

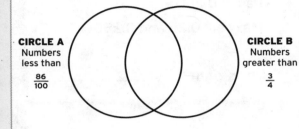

CIRCLE A
Numbers less than
$\frac{86}{100}$

CIRCLE B
Numbers greater than
$\frac{3}{4}$

4

Sort these numbers.

$\frac{4}{5}$, 0.8, $\frac{24}{25}$, 1.0, 0.78, 0.89, $\frac{3}{5}$, 0.25

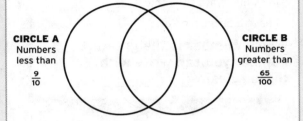

CIRCLE A
Numbers less than
$\frac{9}{10}$

CIRCLE B
Numbers greater than
$\frac{65}{100}$

EXIT Ticket

BLOCK
7

TOPIC 3

Sort these numbers.

$\frac{1}{5}$, 0.5, $\frac{1}{4}$, 0.05, $\frac{4}{10}$, 0.6, $\frac{3}{4}$, 0.75

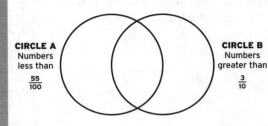

CIRCLE A
Numbers less than
$\frac{55}{100}$

CIRCLE B
Numbers greater than
$\frac{3}{10}$

TOPIC 2

Writing all of the numbers as fractions with a denominator of 100 helps me decide where to place them in the Venn diagram.

TOPIC 1

SCORE ⓪ ① ②

Decimal Place Value

Build It

> Build the greatest number less than 700 that has 9 in the tens place and different digits in each of the other places.

___ 9 ___ . ___ ___

> Explain how you chose digits.

I chose the digits _____

because _____

_____

_____

Brain Teaser

> Solve this riddle.

• I have three different digits (none are 0) and each of them appears twice.

• If you reverse the order of my digits, my value stays the same.

• I have a decimal point.

Which number is the greatest number you can write with these rules? _____

> Explain your reasoning.

The mystery number is _____

because _____

_____

_____

Who's Right?

> Three students are asked to name a decimal that equals $\frac{1}{4}$.

• Aiden: 0.25

• Paula: 0.250

• Maxwell: 0.25 and 0.250

Who's right? _____

> How do you know who's right?

_____ is/are right because

_____

_____

_____

LESSON 4

Which Does Not Belong?
> Circle the number that does not belong.

$\frac{12}{25}$, 0.48, $\frac{24}{50}$, 4.8

> How did you decide which number doesn't belong?

I decided which number doesn't

belong by _____

_____

LESSON 5

Tell Me All That You Can
> About 0.29

- _____
- _____
- _____
- _____

> What is a real-life example that uses the number 0.29?

A real-life example of 0.29 is

_____

_____

Sum It Up!

> In this Topic, you learned how to identify and compare place values in decimal numbers. You also learned how to rename fractions as decimals.

What decimal is equal to $\frac{3}{4}$?

You can rename $\frac{3}{4}$ with a denominator of 100.

$$\frac{3}{4} \times \frac{25}{25} = \frac{75}{100}$$

$$\frac{75}{100} = 0.75$$

LESSON 1
CONCEPT

Use Place Value to Rename Decimals

> WORKED EXAMPLE

> TRY IT

> PRACTICE

STEP 1 Identify the value of digits in a decimal.

765.4321

_7_	hundreds	7×100	700
_6_	tens	6×10	60
_5_	ones	5×1	5
_4_	tenths	$4 \times \frac{1}{10}$	0.4
_3_	hundredths	$3 \times \frac{1}{100}$	0.03

STEP 2 Identify place value patterns.

$$\frac{1}{10} \times 100 = 10$$
$$\frac{1}{10} \times 10 = 1$$
$$\frac{1}{10} \times 1 = \frac{1}{10}$$

Each place value is $\frac{1}{10}$ the value of the place to its left.

STEP 3 Identify places to ten-thousandths.

| _2_ | thousandths | $2 \times \frac{1}{1000}$ | 0.002 |
| _1_ | ten-thousandths | $1 \times \frac{1}{10,000}$ | 0.0001 |

STEP 4 Write the number in expanded form and word form.

Expanded form:
$700 + 60 + 5 + 0.4 + 0.03 + 0.002 + 0.0001$

Word form: seven hundred sixty-five and four thousand three hundred twenty-one ten-thousandths

---

1

STEP 1 Name the place value of each digit.

347.1906

____ hundreds _____ _____

____ tens _____ _____

____ ones _____ _____

____ tenths _____ _____

____ hundredths _____ _____

____ thousandths _____ _____

____ ten-thousandths _____ _____

STEP 2 Write each digit as a product.

STEP 3 Write the number in expanded form.

Expanded form:

_____

STEP 4 Write the number in word form.

Word form:

_____

_____

_____

2

STEP 1 Name the place value of each digit.

40.75

____ tens _____ _____

____ ones _____ _____

____ tenths _____ _____

____ hundredths _____ _____

STEP 2 Write each digit as a product.

STEP 3 Write the number in expanded form.

Expanded form:

STEP 4 Write the number in word form.

Word form:

_____

_____

thousandths place *(n)* the third place to the right of the decimal point, which shows how many thousandths are in a number

> PRACTICE

3

5.12

Expanded form:

_____

_____

Word form:

_____

_____

4

1.375

Expanded form:

_____

Word form:

_____

_____

5

0.635

Expanded form:

_____

Word form:

_____

_____

6

0.1234

Expanded form:

_____

Word form:

_____

_____

7

365.25

Expanded form:

_____

Word form:

_____

_____

8

100.0001

Expanded form:

_____

Word form:

_____

_____

TOPIC 3

> **Solve this problem.**

Write 506.2309 in expanded form and in word form.

Expanded form:

_____

Word form: _____

_____

_____

_____

TOPIC 2

> **How did you write the number in expanded form?**

I wrote the number in expanded

form by _____

_____

_____

_____

TOPIC 1

The value of each digit depends on its place in the number.

SCORE ⓪ ① ②

Identify Patterns in Place Value

> WORKED EXAMPLE   > TRY IT   > PRACTICE

STEP 1 Multiply by 100.

$$3.12 \times 100$$

$(3.12 \times 10) \times 10$

$31.2 \times 10 = 312$

STEP 2 Multiply by 1000.

$$3.12 \times 1000$$

$3.12 \times 10 \times 10 \times 10$

$(3.12 \times 100) \times 10$

$312 \times 10 = 3120$

STEP 3 Divide by 100.

$$63.8 \div 100$$

$(63.8 \div 10) \div 10$

$6.38 \div 10 = 0.638$

STEP 4 Divide by 1000.

$$63.8 \div 1000$$

$63.8 \div 10 \div 10 \div 10$

$(63.8 \div 100) \div 10$

$0.638 \div 10 = 0.0638$

1

STEP 1 Multiply by 100.

$$45.3 \times 100$$

$45.3 \times 100 = \underline{\hspace{2cm}}$

STEP 2 Multiply by 1000.

$$45.3 \times 1000$$

$45.3 \times 1000 = \underline{\hspace{2cm}}$

STEP 3 Divide by 100.

$$53.2 \div 100$$

$53.2 \div 100 = \underline{\hspace{2cm}}$

STEP 4 Divide by 1000.

$$53.2 \div 1000$$

$53.2 \div 1000 = \underline{\hspace{2cm}}$

2

STEP 1 Multiply by 100.

$$4.89 \times 100$$

$4.89 \times 100 = \underline{\hspace{2cm}}$

STEP 2 Multiply by 1000.

$$4.89 \times 1000$$

$4.89 \times 1000 = \underline{\hspace{2cm}}$

STEP 3 Divide by 100.

$$8.2 \div 100$$

$8.2 \div 100 = \underline{\hspace{2cm}}$

STEP 4 Divide by 1000.

$$8.2 \div 1000$$

$8.2 \div 1000 = \underline{\hspace{2cm}}$

3 0.275 × 100

0.275 × 100 = _____

4 100.5 ÷ 100

100.5 ÷ 100 = _____

5 14.75 × 1000

14.75 × 1000 = _____

6 25.01 ÷ 1000

25.01 ÷ 1000 = _____

7 45.45 ÷ 1000

45.45 ÷ 1000 = _____

8 0.01 × 1000

0.01 × 1000 = _____

9 75.22 ÷ 1000

75.22 ÷ 1000 = _____

10 125.6 × 100

125.6 × 100 = _____

EXIT Ticket

BLOCK
7

> **Find the errors and fix the math.**

34.1 × 1000

34.1 × 10 × 10 × 10

0.341 × 10

34.1 × 1000 = 3.41

> **Explain the error and how you fixed it.**

The error was _____

_____

_____

I fixed the error by _____

_____

_____

TOPIC 3

TOPIC 2

TOPIC 1

Multiplying by 10 increases the place value of each digit by a factor of 10.

SCORE ⓪ ① ②

Divide to Name Fractions as Decimals

> WORKED EXAMPLE

> TRY IT

> PRACTICE

WORKED EXAMPLE

STEP 1 Rename the fraction.

Rename $\frac{3}{8}$ as a decimal.

Division: $8 \overline{)\ 3}$

STEP 2 Multiply the dividend.

$\underline{\quad 3 \quad} \times \underline{\ 1000\ } = \underline{\ 3000\ }$

STEP 3 Divide with partial quotients.

$$
\begin{array}{r}
5 \\
70 \qquad 375 \\
300 \\
8 \overline{)\ 3000} \\
-2400 \\
\hline
600 \\
-560 \\
\hline
40 \\
-40 \\
\hline
0
\end{array}
$$

STEP 4 Divide the quotient.

$\underline{\ 375\ } \div \underline{\ 1000\ } = \frac{375}{1000}$

$\frac{375}{1000} = \underline{0.375}$

$\frac{3}{8} = \underline{0.375}$

TRY IT

1

STEP 1 Write the fraction as division.

Rename $\frac{7}{4}$ as a decimal.

Division:

STEP 2 Multiply the dividend.

$\underline{\qquad} \times \underline{\qquad} = \underline{\qquad}$

STEP 3 Divide with partial quotients.

STEP 4 Divide the quotient.

$\underline{\qquad} \div \underline{\qquad} = \underline{\qquad}$

$\underline{\qquad} = \underline{\qquad}$

$\frac{7}{4} = \underline{\qquad}$

PRACTICE

2

STEP 1 Write the fraction as division.

Rename $\frac{7}{8}$ as a decimal.

Division:

STEP 2 Multiply the dividend.

$\underline{\qquad} \times \underline{\qquad} = \underline{\qquad}$

STEP 3 Divide with partial quotients.

STEP 4 Divide the quotient.

$\underline{\qquad} \div \underline{\qquad} = \underline{\qquad}$

$\underline{\qquad} = \underline{\qquad}$

$\frac{7}{8} = \underline{\qquad}$

partial quotient *(n)* numbers you add to calculate a quotient

3

Rename $\frac{1}{8}$ as a decimal.

Division:

_____ × _____ = _____

_____ ÷ _____ = _____

_____ = _____

$\frac{1}{8}$ = _____

4

Rename $\frac{13}{5}$ as a decimal.

Division:

_____ × _____ = _____

_____ ÷ _____ = _____

_____ = _____

$\frac{13}{5}$ = _____

EXIT Ticket

BLOCK **7**

> **Solve this problem.**

Rename $\frac{5}{8}$ as a decimal. Show your work.

Division:

_____ × _____ = _____

TOPIC 3

TOPIC 2

_____ ÷ _____ = _____

$\frac{5}{8}$ = _____

TOPIC 1

> **Explain how you solved this problem.**

I solved this problem by

_____

_____

_____

_____

SCORE ⓪ ① ②

Develop Strategies With Decimals

When my grid is close to being filled, I won't roll again in this game.

RULES

Over & Out (Level 2)

What You Need
- *mSpace* pages 118–121
- decahedron (black, 0–9)

What to Know
- Players fill as much of the decimal grid as possible.
- Stop when you think your grid is filled enough to win.
- Once a player has decided to stop, turns cannot be made afterwards.

How to Win
- The first player to fill the decimal grid in 5 turns wins.
- If both players have stopped, the player whose grid is closest to being filled is the winner.
- If a player goes over shading one grid, the other player wins.

> HOW TO PLAY

STEP 1 Roll the decahedron and record that number.

NUMBERS ROLLED	DECIMALS USED

STEP 2 Decide whether the number rolled should be a decimal in the tenths or the hundredths place.

NUMBERS ROLLED	DECIMALS USED
6	0.6

STEP 3 Shade the decimal in the grid.

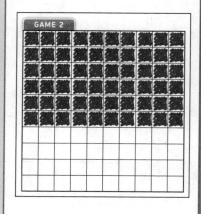

GAME 2

STEP 4 Take turns with your partner.

RECORDING SHEET

Over & Out (Level 2)

› Record the numbers you rolled and shade the grid with the decimals chosen.
Optional: Use the grid paper on page 121 for calculations.

GAME 1

NUMBERS ROLLED	DECIMALS USED

GAME 2

NUMBERS ROLLED	DECIMALS USED

GAME 3

NUMBERS ROLLED	DECIMALS USED

GAME 4

NUMBERS ROLLED	DECIMALS USED

RECORDING SHEET
Over & Out (Level 2)

> Record the numbers you rolled and shade the grid with the decimals chosen. Optional: Use the grid paper on page 121 for calculations.

BLOCK 7

GAME 1

NUMBERS ROLLED	DECIMALS USED

GAME 2

NUMBERS ROLLED	DECIMALS USED

GAME 3

NUMBERS ROLLED	DECIMALS USED

GAME 4

NUMBERS ROLLED	DECIMALS USED

> **Optional: Use this space for calculations.**

TOPIC 3

> **Answer this question.**

Your second roll is 5. Will you choose tenths or hundredths?

NUMBERS ROLLED	DECIMALS USED
2	0.2
5	

If I rolled 5, I would choose

_____ because _____

_____

_____

SCORE ⓪ ① ②

TOPIC 2

CAREER EXPLORATION

> **Civil engineers design buildings, roads, bridges, and dams.**

Do you think engineers use fractions, decimals, or both?

TOPIC 1

LESSON 5
PROBLEM SOLVING

Solve Problems With Decimals

STEP 1 Analyze the problem.

A long jump athlete's training distances are 8.4 m, 7.04 m, 7.46 m, 8.41 m, and 7.3 m. List the distances in order from least to greatest.

STEP 2 Rename the decimals.

8.40 m   7.04 m   7.46 m

8.41 m   7.30 m

STEP 3 Use place value to order the decimals.

The distances in order from least to greatest are

7.04 m   7.3 m   7.46 m

8.4 m   8.41 m

STEP 4 Check your work.

1

STEP 1 Analyze the problem.

In an Olympics women's 400-meter freestyle race, one swimmer completed the race in 4 minutes 3.52 seconds. Another swimmer raced in 4 minutes 3.6 seconds. Which was the faster time?

STEP 2 Rename the decimals.

STEP 3 Use place value to order the decimals.

_____ ☐ _____

The faster time is _____

_____

STEP 4 Check your work.

2

STEP 1 Analyze the problem.

Until Usain Bolt broke the record for the men's 200-meter race, the top times were 20.4 sec, 19.3 sec, 19.96 sec, 19.98 sec, and 20.22 sec. List the times in order from fastest to slowest.

STEP 2 Rename the decimals.

STEP 3 Use place value to order the decimals.

The times in order from fastest to slowest are

_____

_____

STEP 4 Check your work.

3

In the men's bike race at the 2012 Olympics, two riders had times of 36.19 seconds and 36.606 seconds. Which was the faster time?

The faster time is _____

_____

4

At the 2012 Olympics, the top five scores for women's balance beam were 16.025, 15.9, 15.625, 16.225, and 15.95. List the scores in order from greatest to least.

The scores in order from greatest to least are

_____

_____

BLOCK
7

> **Solve this problem.**

Michael Phelps broke his own world record for the 400-meter individual medley swim at the 2008 Olympic trials. His times were 4 minutes 5.25 seconds and 4 minutes 6.22 seconds. Which was the faster time?

The faster time is _____

_____

> Renaming numbers so that they have the same number of decimal places helps me to compare the numbers.

TOPIC 3

TOPIC 2

TOPIC 1

SCORE ⓪ ① ②

LESSON 1

Tell Me All That You Can

> About 1.65

- _____
- _____
- _____
- _____
- _____
- _____

> Jake said, "You can write 1.65 as 1.6500." Do you agree with him?

I agree/disagree with Jake

because _____

_____

LESSON 2

Brain Teaser

> Solve this riddle.

- I am less than halfway between 0.5 and 0.6.

- My hundredths digit is even.

- I am not 0.52.

Which decimal am I? _____

> What was the first step you took to solve the riddle?

My first step was to _____

_____

_____

LESSON 3

Missing Numbers

> Write the missing numbers to complete both patterns.

A. 1, $\frac{1}{2}$, $\frac{1}{4}$, $\boxed{}$, $\frac{1}{16}$, $\frac{1}{32}$, $\boxed{}$

B. 3000, 300, _____, 3, 0.3, _____, 0.003

> How are the two patterns alike?

The two patterns are alike because

_____

_____

_____

Who's Right?

> Three students were asked to name a decimal between 3.34 and 3.46.

- Fiona: 3.4
- Diana: 3.5
- Sarah: Both Fiona and Diana are correct.

Who's right? _____

> **How do you know who's right?**

I know _____ is right because

_____

_____

_____

Find the Pattern

> Find the rule. Then, write a number in the circle using the rule.

0.25

0.11

0.3

0.5

0.700

0.20

0.22

0.74

> **Why does the number you wrote belong in the circle?**

I wrote _____ in the circle

because _____

_____

_____

Sum It Up!

> In this Topic, you learned to compare decimals and locate them on a number line.

How can I find decimals between 0.4 and 0.5?

Use a number line to locate decimals between 0.40 and 0.50.

0.40 0.41 0.42 0.43 0.44 0.45 0.46 0.47 0.48 0.49 0.50

> WORKED EXAMPLE

> TRY IT

> PRACTICE

STEP 1 Label the tenths between 0 and 1.

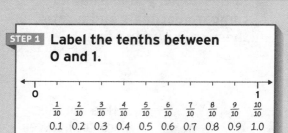

STEP 2 Name the tenths as hundredths.

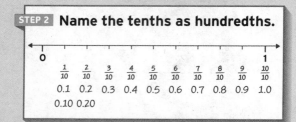

STEP 3 Locate hundredths on a number line.

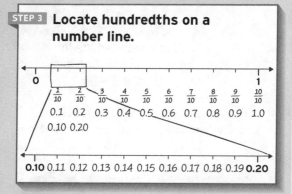

1

STEP 1 Locate a decimal between tenths on a number line.

Plot 0.24 on the number line.

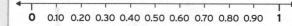

STEP 2 Prepare a number line for hundredths.

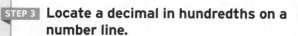

STEP 3 Locate a decimal in hundredths on a number line.

2

STEP 1 Locate a decimal between tenths on a number line.

Plot 0.76 on the number line.

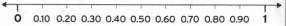

STEP 2 Prepare a number line for hundredths.

STEP 3 Locate a decimal in hundredths on a number line.

3 Plot 2.12 on the number lines.

```
←+--+--+--+--+--+--+--+--+--+--→
 2.0                         3.0
```

```
←+--+--+--+--+--+--+--+--+--+--→
 2.10                       2.20
```

4 Plot 3.05 on the number lines.

```
←+--+--+--+--+--+--+--+--+--+--→
 3.0                         4.0
```

```
←+--+--+--+--+--+--+--+--+--+--→
 3.00                       3.10
```

5 Plot 3.54 on the number lines.

```
←+--+--+--+--+--+--+--+--+--+--→
 3.0                         4.0
```

```
←+--+--+--+--+--+--+--+--+--+--→
 3.50                       3.60
```

6 Plot 2.57 on the number lines.

```
←+--+--+--+--+--+--+--+--+--+--→
 2.0                         3.0
```

```
←+--+--+--+--+--+--+--+--+--+--→
 2.50                       2.60
```

7 Plot 9.87 on the number lines.

```
←+--+--+--+--+--+--+--+--+--+--→
 9.0                        10.0
```

```
←+--+--+--+--+--+--+--+--+--+--→
 9.80                       9.90
```

8 Plot 6.36 on the number lines.

```
←+--+--+--+--+--+--+--+--+--+--→
 6.0                         7.0
```

```
←+--+--+--+--+--+--+--+--+--+--→
 6.30                       6.40
```

EXIT Ticket

> **Solve this problem.**

Plot 0.60, 0.63, and 0.69 on the number line.

```
←+--+--+--+--+--+--+--+--+--+--→
 0.6                         0.7
```

> **Why do these numbers belong between 0.6 and 0.7 on the number line?**

These numbers belong between 0.6 and 0.7 because _____

_____

_____

I can use a number line to show the location of any number.

TOPIC 3

TOPIC 2

TOPIC 1

SCORE ⓪ ① ②

> WORKED EXAMPLE

> TRY IT

> PRACTICE

BLOCK 7

STEP 1 Rename decimals as fractions.

$$0.107 \boxed{<} 0.17$$

$$0.107 = \frac{107}{1000} \qquad 0.17 = \frac{17}{100}$$

$$\frac{17 \times 10}{100 \times 10} = \frac{170}{1000}$$

STEP 2 Compare using common denominators.

$$\frac{107}{1000} < \frac{170}{1000}$$

$$0.107 < 0.17$$

STEP 3 Compare by writing digits to the same place value.

$$0.17 = 0.170$$

$$0.107 < 0.170$$

$$0.107 < 0.17$$

1

STEP 1 Rename decimals as fractions.

$$1.006 \boxed{\phantom{<}} 1.01$$

1.006 = _____   1.01 = _____

STEP 2 Compare using common denominators.

STEP 3 Compare by writing digits to the same place value.

1.006 = _____   1.01 = _____

2

STEP 1 Rename decimals as fractions.

$$0.1 \boxed{\phantom{<}} 1.05$$

0.1 = _____   1.05 = _____

STEP 2 Compare using common denominators.

STEP 3 Compare by writing digits to the same place value.

0.1 = _____   1.05 = _____

I usually compare decimals by renaming them as fractions.

3

4.125 ☐ 4.5

4

9.9 ☐ 9.99

5

3.005 ☐ 3.02

6

3.15 ☐ 2.55

7

0.586 ☐ 0.685

8

0.737 ☐ 0.736

EXIT Ticket

BLOCK **7**

> **Solve this problem.**

Compare:

0.549 ☐ 0.551

TOPIC 3

TOPIC 2

> **Which method do you prefer to compare decimals?**

I prefer to compare decimals by

_____

_____ because

TOPIC 1

_____

_____

_____

_____

SCORE ⓪ ① ②

> WORKED EXAMPLE

> TRY IT

> PRACTICE

STEP 1 Name decimals between whole numbers.

Locate 21.116

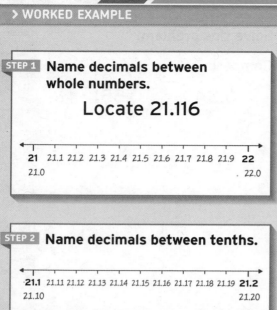

STEP 2 Name decimals between tenths.

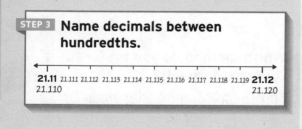

STEP 3 Name decimals between hundredths.

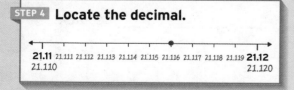

STEP 4 Locate the decimal.

1

STEP 1 Name decimals between whole numbers.

Locate 3.155

STEP 2 Name decimals between tenths.

STEP 3 Name decimals between hundredths.

STEP 4 Locate the decimal.

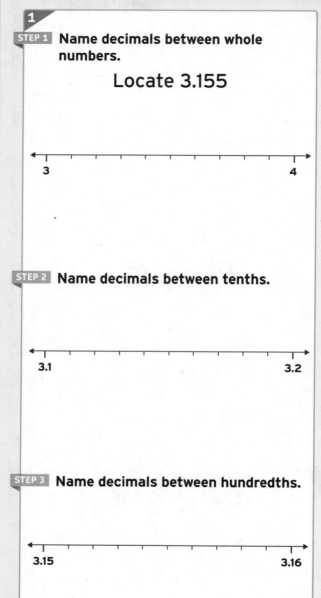

2

STEP 1 Name decimals between whole numbers.

Locate 1.823

STEP 2 Name decimals between tenths.

STEP 3 Name decimals between hundredths.

STEP 4 Locate the decimal.

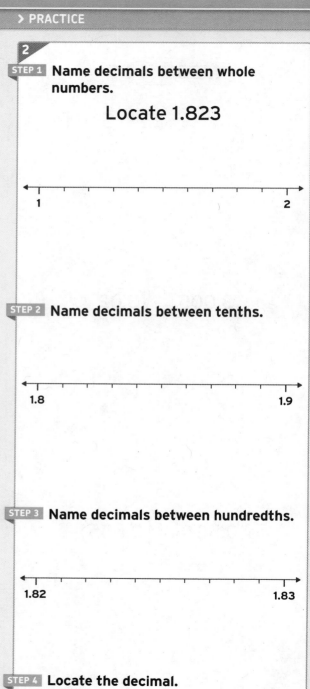

3 Locate 0.332

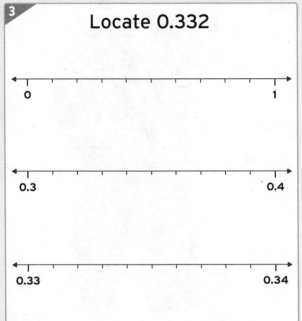

4 Locate 0.928

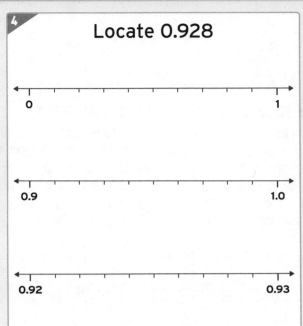

5 Locate 12.256

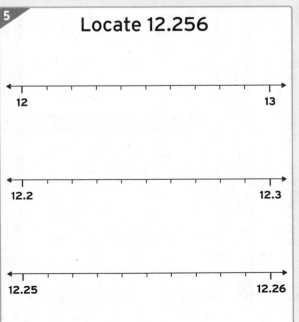

6 Locate 52.297

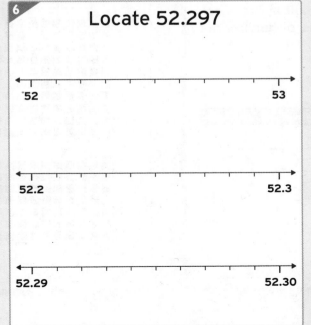

EXIT Ticket

BLOCK **7**

> **Find the error and fix the math.**

Locate 0.206

0.2 0.201 0.202 0.203 0.204 0.205 0.206 0.207 0.208 0.209 0.3

TOPIC 3

Explain the error and how you fixed it.

The error in this problem was

_____

_____

_____

_____

I fixed the error by _____

_____

_____

_____

_____

TOPIC 2

TOPIC 1

SCORE ⓪ ① ②

Use Reasoning With Decimals

Can I win the game with only one roll?

RULES

Over & Out (Level 3)

What You Need
- *mSpace* pages 132–135
- decahedron (black, 0–9)

What to Know
- Players fill as much of two decimal grids as possible in five rolls.
- Players may stop before five turns. Once stopped, a player cannot take any more turns.

How to Win
- The first player to fill two grids in five turns is the winner.
- If both players stop, the player closest to filling 2 grids wins.
- If a player needs to shade more than two grids, the other player wins.

> HOW TO PLAY

STEP 1 Roll the decahedron and record that number.

NUMBERS ROLLED	DECIMALS USED
1	1
7	

STEP 2 Decide whether the number rolled should be a digit in the ones, tenths, or hundredths place.

NUMBERS ROLLED	DECIMALS USED
1	1
7	0.7

STEP 3 Shade the decimal in the grid.

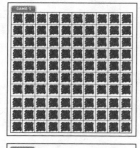
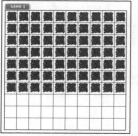

STEP 4 Record an addition equation.

EQUATION
0 + 1 = 1
1 + 0.7 = 1.7

RECORDING SHEET

Over & Out (Level 3)

> Record the numbers rolled and your equations.
> Optional: Use the grid paper on page 135 to play additional games.

GAME 1

NUMBERS ROLLED	DECIMALS USED	EQUATION

BLOCK 7 › TOPIC 3
LESSON 4

RECORDING SHEET
Over & Out (Level 3)

› Record the numbers rolled and your equations.
Optional: Use the grid paper on page 135 to play additional games.

BLOCK 7

GAME 2

NUMBERS ROLLED	DECIMALS USED	EQUATION

> **Optional: Use this space to play additional games.**

> **Answer this question.**

When is it a good idea to put the number you rolled in the ones place?

It is a good idea to put the number you rolled in the ones place if _____

_____

_____

_____

SCORE ⓪ ① ②

CAREER EXPLORATION

> **Broadcast technicians use decimals to position cameras.**

Why might technicians choose decimals instead of fractions to measure distance?

LESSON 5
PROBLEM SOLVING

Solve Decimal Problems With Equivalence

> WORKED EXAMPLE

> TRY IT

> PRACTICE

STEP 1 Analyze the problem.

What is the value of k in pounds?

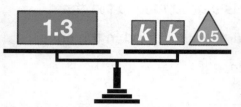

STEP 2 Write an equation for the problem.

$$1.3 = k + k + 0.5$$

STEP 3 Solve the problem.

$$\frac{13}{10} = k + k + \frac{5}{10}$$

$$k + k = \frac{8}{10}$$

$$2k = 0.8$$

$$k = 0.4 \text{ lb}$$

STEP 4 Check your work.

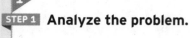

STEP 1 Analyze the problem.

What is the value of n in ounces?

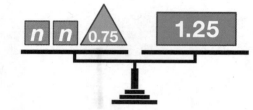

STEP 2 Write an equation for the problem.

STEP 3 Solve the problem.

STEP 4 Check your work.

2

STEP 1 Analyze the problem.

What is the value of p in kilograms?

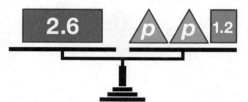

STEP 2 Write an equation for the problem.

STEP 3 Solve the problem.

STEP 4 Check your work.

BLOCK 7

3

STEP 1 Analyze the problem.

What is the value of *n* in pounds?

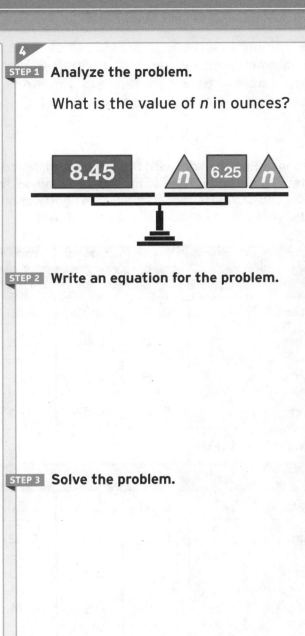

STEP 2 Write an equation for the problem.

STEP 3 Solve the problem.

STEP 4 Check your work.

4

STEP 1 Analyze the problem.

What is the value of *n* in ounces?

STEP 2 Write an equation for the problem.

STEP 3 Solve the problem.

STEP 4 Check your work.

EXIT
Ticket

> Solve this problem.

What is the value of *k* in pounds?

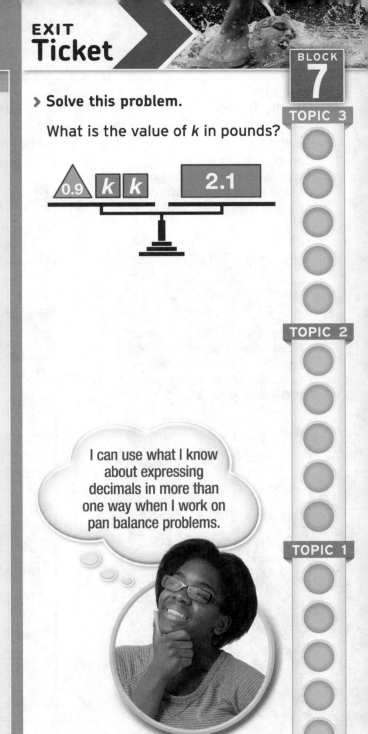

I can use what I know about expressing decimals in more than one way when I work on pan balance problems.

BLOCK

7

TOPIC 3

TOPIC 2

TOPIC 1

SCORE ⓪ ① ②

> **YOUR JOB**
Athletic Trainer

> **YOUR TASK**
Compare data on trial races, and then set target distances to help runners improve their race times.

ANCHOR VIDEO CONNECTION

As the Anchor Video shows, a fraction of a second could mean the difference between a gold and silver medal at the Olympic Games.

Train Olympic Athletes

> You are training two track-and-field athletes for the 1.5-kilometer race in the next Olympic Games. Help them improve their race times to 3 minutes, 30 seconds—a time that should win a medal.

A EXPLORE

For each runner, find the trial with the greatest distance at 3 minutes, 30 seconds. Then enter target distances for every 30 seconds. Choose targets that are slightly greater than the distances in the runner's best overall trial.

Runner's Distance Every 30 Seconds							
Runner A							
Time (min:sec)	**0:30**	**1:00**	**1:30**	**2:00**	**2:30**	**3:00**	**3:30**
Trial 1 (km)	0.18	0.40	0.58	0.77	0.92	1.12	1.24
Trial 2 (km)	0.09	0.20	0.38	0.66	0.90	1.18	1.43
Trial 3 (km)	0.25	0.52	0.74	0.93	1.12	1.27	1.32
Target Distances (km)							1.50
Runner B							
Time (min:sec)	**0:30**	**1:00**	**1:30**	**2:00**	**2:30**	**3:00**	**3:30**
Trial 1 (km)	0.20	0.41	0.62	0.82	1.03	1.24	1.45
Trial 2 (km)	0.13	0.28	0.45	0.61	0.85	1.07	1.28
Trial 3 (km)	0.28	0.56	0.74	0.90	1.06	1.17	1.22
Target Distances (km)							1.50

Create a double line graph to compare your target distances for the two runners. Label one line Runner A and the other line Runner B.

To draw a line, begin by plotting one point for each time. The height of the point shows the target distance. The points for the start and finish times are plotted for you. Then draw a line to connect the points.

Target Race Distances for Two Runners

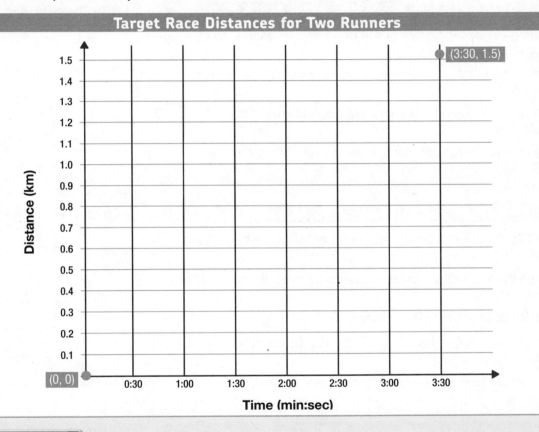

C ANALYZE

EXPLAIN How do you know which trial was fastest for each runner? Which trials were the fastest?

_____

_____

_____

INTERPRET If the two runners meet their target distances, describe a race between them.

_____

_____

_____

Evaluate

▸ Rate how well you and your partner understood and completed each part of the performance task:

Rating Scale			
None	Limited	Partial	Thorough
0	1	2	3

A Entered target distances for two runners.

Me	0	1	2	3
Partner	0	1	2	3

B Created a double line graph for the two target distances.

Me	0	1	2	3
Partner	0	1	2	3

C Answered each question accurately.

Me	0	1	2	3
Partner	0	1	2	3

EXTEND

Help train a runner for the 100-meter dash. Set target distances every second for finishing the race in 10 seconds. Make a line graph to show your results. Use extra graph paper to show your work.

Reflect on Your Learning Strategies

Congratulations! You've completed Block 7 of *MATH 180*.
Respond to these questions by checking EACH sentence
that describes your mindset.

A CHALLENGE SEEKING

When you take on new challenges, you learn more and your brain becomes stronger and smarter.

What challenges did you set for yourself and meet during BLOCK 7 ?

- ☐ I set a goal to complete a specific number of Brain Arcade games, and I met or exceeded that goal.
- ☐ I checked my solutions to all of the math problems I solved, and I corrected any mistakes I made.
- ☐ I participated in class discussions, asked questions, and shared my thoughts and opinions.
- ☐ I studied for the *mSkills* assessment by reviewing every Block 7 lesson.

☐ Other *(please describe)*:

_____

_____

_____

_____

B EFFORT, PRACTICE, AND PERSISTENCE

Practice is like exercise for your brain. Keep practicing, and you will develop your "brain muscle" over time.

How did you build and deepen your knowledge of BLOCK 7 math concepts?

- ☐ I asked a classmate, my teacher, or a family member for help when I didn't understand something.
- ☐ I tried new strategies for solving problems, especially when old strategies seemed to work poorly.
- ☐ I solved every practice problem in the *mSpace*.
- ☐ I asked myself questions or discussed my questions with a partner to make sure I understood a math concept.
- ☐ I worked with a partner to invent and then solve math problems.

☐ Other *(please describe)*:

_____

_____

_____

_____

_____

C LEARNING FROM MISTAKES AND FEEDBACK

Mistakes can help you learn if you recognize and correct them.

How did you respond to mistakes you made on BLOCK 7 math problems?

- ☐ I reminded myself to think positive instead of negative thoughts.
- ☐ I discussed ways to improve my math skills with my teacher or a classmate.
- ☐ I reminded myself that I can learn from mistakes.
- ☐ I looked for ways to avoid making the same mistake on similar problems.
- ☐ I practiced calming strategies like taking deep breaths, remembering a fun time, or thinking of things I enjoy doing.

☐ Other *(please describe)*:

_____

_____

_____

_____

_____

Score Your Mindset

> **Count up all your checks and write the total here:**

TOTAL CHECKS

If you checked . . .	You were in the following zone, which means . . .

Less than 3

Fixed Mindset Zone
You didn't use many brain-wise learning strategies this time. Your mindset may have held you back from doing your best.

3–5

Mixed Mindset Zone
You used some good strategies but skipped some others. Your mindset may have held you back from doing your best.

6 or more

Growth Mindset Zone
Overall, your use of learning strategies was in the Growth Mindset Zone this time. You used many good strategies that will help your brain grow and get smarter.

> **What can you do about it?**

- Review the strategies listed in the Mindset Scan.
- Choose one strategy from each category that you think would help you learn. Copy these strategies into your journal or notebook.
- Try each strategy as you study the math concepts of the next Block.

Brain Boosting

> **What will you do to help your brain stay in the Growth Mindset Zone?**

I will focus on:

- ☐ Challenge-seeking
- ☐ Effort, practice, and persistence
- ☐ Learning from mistakes and feedback

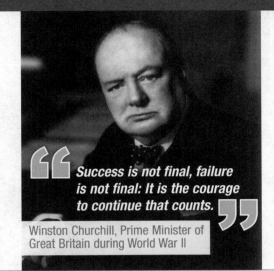

Success is not final, failure is not final: It is the courage to continue that counts.

Winston Churchill, Prime Minister of Great Britain during World War II

What will I do?

_____
_____
_____
_____

Who will help me?

_____
_____
_____
_____

When will I do it?

_____
_____
_____
_____

How will this help me to grow?

_____
_____
_____
_____

VOCABULARY

addend

difference

Distributive Property

expanded form

factor

partial product

quotient

variable

Dollars and Sense

Do you have a great idea for a business?

In this Anchor Video, young entrepreneurs turn smart ideas into booming businesses.

Math in Business

In this Block, you will explore how math is used in business and management.

Are you good with money?

FINANCIAL Advisors

use all areas of mathematics to help people and businesses decide how to best invest their funds.

Accountants

prepare financial records and taxes. By **2020**, there will be **1.4 million** accountants in the United States.

REAL ESTATE Agents

help clients buy, sell, and rent properties. They earn most of their income on commission, which is a **percentage** of the property's sales price.

FOOD SERVICE Managers

run restaurants. They often work **12–15 hours per day** and **6–7 days per week**.

Do you have a great idea for a new product or service?

Entrepreneurs

take their clever ideas and turn them into new businesses.

LESSON 1

Block Preview

› **Think about the Anchor Video and answer this question.**

What business would you like to start in your community?

› **Explain your strategy.**

I would like to start a business

that _____ because

_____

_____

LESSON 2

Make an Estimate

› **Estimate the six sums. Then order them from least to greatest. The letters will spell a math word.**

S = 58.17 + 41.62   N = 26.132 + 17.322

T = 39.77 + 31.42   E = 18.82 + 3.88

T = 10.37 + 10.48   H = 38.06 + 45.19

____ ____ ____ ____ ____ ____

› **Why is estimation useful for solving this problem?**

Estimation is useful because

_____

_____

_____

LESSON 3

Who's Right?

› **Kerry and Jing used an open number line to find $2\frac{5}{8} - 1\frac{1}{2}$.**

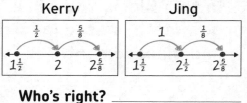

Kerry   Jing

Who's right? _____

› **Explain your answer.**

The number line is used correctly

by _____ because

_____

_____

_____

LESSON 4

Missing Numbers

> Choose numbers from the list to make the best estimates.

- Estimate: _____ − 12.58 is about 10.
- Estimate: _____ − 9.16 is about 12.
- Estimate: _____ − 6.28 is about 16.
- Estimate: _____ − 15.7 is about 8.

24.09   21.82   23.15   20.78

> What strategy did you use to find the missing numbers?

I found the missing numbers by

_____

_____

_____

LESSON 5

Brain Teaser

> Solve this riddle.

- I am a decimal in hundredths.
- Add 1.5 to me for a sum of 2.75.
- Subtract 0.2 from me for a difference of 1.05.

What number am I? _____

> Explain how you found the mystery number.

I found the mystery number by

_____

_____

_____

> In this Topic, you learned to add and subtract decimals. Estimates help you make sure your answer is reasonable.

If you add 3.41 and 64.8 to find a sum of 98.9, how do you know that's wrong?

The addends are close to 3 and 65, so the sum should be close to 68.

3.41 + 64.8

Estimate: _____3 + 65 = 68_____

Apply Place Value to Add Decimals

> WORKED EXAMPLE

STEP 1 Make an estimate.

$$5.76 + 7.23$$

Estimate: $6 + 7 = 13$

STEP 2 Write addends in expanded form.

Expanded form: $5 + 0.7 + 0.06$
$7 + 0.2 + 0.03$

STEP 3 Add using place value.

$$
\begin{array}{r}
5 + 0.7 + 0.06 \\
+\,7 + 0.2 + 0.03 \\
\hline
12 + 0.9 + 0.09
\end{array}
$$

STEP 4 Add the partial sums.

$$
\begin{array}{r}
12 \\
0.9 \\
+\,0.09 \\
\hline
12.99
\end{array}
$$

$$5.76 + 7.23 = \underline{12.99}$$

Is your answer reasonable? _yes_

> TRY IT

1

STEP 1 Make an estimate.

$$6.95 + 7.76$$

Estimate: _____

STEP 2 Write addends in expanded form.

Expanded form:

STEP 3 Add using place value.

STEP 4 Add the partial sums.

$$6.95 + 7.76 = \underline{}$$

Is your answer reasonable? _____

> PRACTICE

2

STEP 1 Make an estimate.

$$10.13 + 8.69$$

Estimate: _____

STEP 2 Write addends in expanded form.

Expanded form:

STEP 3 Add using place value.

STEP 4 Add the partial sums.

$$10.13 + 8.69 = \underline{}$$

Is your answer reasonable? _____

BLOCK 8

expanded form *(n)* a number written as the sum of the values of each digit based on its place value

> PRACTICE

3

$$4.81 + 11.75$$

Estimate: _____

Expanded form:

$$4.81 + 11.75 = \underline{\hspace{1cm}}$$

Is your answer reasonable? _____

4

$$15.79 + 10.87$$

Estimate: _____

Expanded form:

$$15.79 + 10.87 = \underline{\hspace{1cm}}$$

Is your answer reasonable? _____

> **Find the sum.**

TOPIC 3

$$13.42 + 7.88$$

Estimate: _____

Expanded form:

$$13.42 + 7.88 = \underline{\hspace{1cm}}$$

Is your answer reasonable?_____

TOPIC 2

TOPIC 1

> **How do you know your answer is reasonable?**

I know my answer is reasonable

because _____

_____

_____

 SCORE ⓪ ① ②

LESSON 2
CONCEPT

Add Decimals

> WORKED EXAMPLE

> TRY IT

> PRACTICE

Worked Example

STEP 1 Make an estimate.

$$10.12 + 9.22$$

Estimate: $\underline{10 + 9 = 19}$

STEP 2 Add using place value.

$$
\begin{array}{r}
10.12 \\
+ \ 9.22 \\
\hline
10 \\
9 \\
0.3 \\
0.04 \\
\end{array}
$$

STEP 3 Add the partial sums.

$$
\begin{array}{r}
10 \\
9 \\
0.3 \\
+ \ 0.04 \\
\hline
19.34 \\
\end{array}
$$

$$10.12 + 9.22 = \underline{19.34}$$

STEP 4 Compare the sum and estimate.

Is your answer reasonable? $\underline{yes}$

1

STEP 1 Make an estimate.

$$22.78 + 12.39$$

Estimate: _____

STEP 2 Add using place value.

STEP 3 Add the partial sums.

$$22.78 + 12.39 = \underline{\hspace{1cm}}$$

STEP 4 Compare the sum and estimate.

Is your answer reasonable? _____

2

STEP 1 Make an estimate.

$$14.94 + 5.09$$

Estimate: _____

STEP 2 Add using place value.

STEP 3 Add the partial sums.

$$14.94 + 5.09 = \underline{\hspace{1cm}}$$

STEP 4 Compare the sum and estimate.

Is your answer reasonable? _____

BLOCK 8

> PRACTICE

3

$3.44 + 1.7$

Estimate: _____

$3.44 + 1.7 =$ _____

Is your answer reasonable? _____

4

$5.80 + 3.75$

Estimate: _____

$5.80 + 3.75 =$ _____

Is your answer reasonable? _____

5

$1.9 + 99.41$

Estimate: _____

$1.9 + 99.41 =$ _____

Is your answer reasonable? _____

6

$0.06 + 5.98$

Estimate: _____

$0.06 + 5.98 =$ _____

Is your answer reasonable? _____

EXIT Ticket

BLOCK
8

> **Find the error and fix the math.**

$16.83 + 21.45$

$$\begin{array}{r} 16.83 \\ + 21.45 \\ \hline 30.00 \\ 7.00 \\ + 0.12 \\ \hline 0.08 \\ \hline 37.20 \end{array}$$

TOPIC 3

TOPIC 2

> **What is the error and how did you fix it? Explain your thinking.**

The error was _____

_____

_____

_____

I fixed it by _____

_____

_____

_____

TOPIC 1

SCORE ⓪ ① ②

Adding and Subtracting Decimals **147**

Use Models to Subtract Decimals

> WORKED EXAMPLE | > TRY IT | > PRACTICE

STEP 1 Make an estimate.

$$3.84 - 1.22$$

Estimate: _4 – 1 = 3_

STEP 2 Subtract with an open number line.

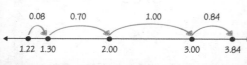

0.08   0.70   1.00   0.84

1.22 1.30   2.00   3.00   3.84

STEP 3 Add the jumps.

$$
\begin{array}{r}
0.08 \\
0.70 \\
1.00 \\
+ \ 0.84 \\
\hline
1.00 \\
1.5 \\
+ \ 0.12 \\
\hline
2.62
\end{array}
$$

$$3.84 - 1.22 = \underline{2.62}$$

STEP 4 Compare the difference to the estimate.

Is your answer reasonable? _yes_

1

STEP 1 Make an estimate.

$$10.34 - 4.85$$

Estimate: _____

STEP 2 Subtract with an open number line.

⟵————————————————⟶

STEP 3 Add the jumps.

$$10.34 - 4.85 = \underline{\hspace{1.5cm}}$$

STEP 4 Compare the difference to the estimate.

Is your answer reasonable? _____

2

STEP 1 Make an estimate.

$$2.4 - 0.89$$

Estimate: _____

STEP 2 Subtract with an open number line.

⟵————————————————⟶

STEP 3 Add the jumps.

$$2.4 - 0.89 = \underline{\hspace{1.5cm}}$$

STEP 4 Compare the difference to the estimate.

Is your answer reasonable? _____

BLOCK 8

> First I jump to the closest tenth, and then to the closest whole number.

3

$$8.44 - 3.17$$

Estimate: _____

<--------------------------------->

Is your answer reasonable? _____

4

$$11.10 - 7.14$$

Estimate: _____

<--------------------------------->

Is your answer reasonable? _____

5

$$10.95 - 3.70$$

Estimate: _____

<--------------------------------->

Is your answer reasonable? _____

6

$$8.6 - 4.05$$

Estimate: _____

<--------------------------------->

Is your answer reasonable? _____

EXIT Ticket

BLOCK **8**

TOPIC 3

> **Find the difference.**

$$1.71 - 0.76$$

Estimate: _____

<--------------------------------->

TOPIC 2

$$1.71 - 0.76 = _____$$

Is your answer reasonable? _____

> **Which benchmark did you jump to first? Explain.**

TOPIC 1

I jumped to a benchmark of _____ first because _____

_____

_____

_____

_____

SCORE ⓪ ① ②

LESSON 4
GAME

Develop Number Sense With Decimals

I can't skip a turn, so I'll try not to get too close to zero in the early rounds.

RULES
Decimal Dare (Level 1)

What You Need
- *mSpace* pages 150–153
- decahedron (black, 0–9)

What to Know
- The starting number is 50.
- There are 6 rounds in a game. You may not skip a round.

How to Win
- The winner is the player who gets closest to zero without going below.

> HOW TO PLAY

STEP 1 Roll the decahedron two times.

Roll 1   Roll 2

STEP 2 Use the two numbers to make a whole number or a decimal.

Whole Number:
62 or 26

Decimal: 2.6 or 6.2

0.26 or 0.62

GAME 1			
ROUND	NUMBERS ROLLED	NUMBER CHOSEN	SUBTRACTION
1	6, 2	26	
2			
3			

STEP 3 Subtract the number from 50 or from the difference from your last round.

GAME 1			
ROUND	NUMBERS ROLLED	NUMBER CHOSEN	SUBTRACTION
1	6, 2	26	50 − 26 = 24
2			
3			

STEP 4 Record the difference and take turns.

GAME 1			
ROUND	NUMBERS ROLLED	NUMBER CHOSEN	SUBTRACTION
1	6, 2	26	50 − 26 = 24
2	5, 6	6.5	24 − 6.5 = 17.5
3	2, 5	2.5	17.5 − 2.5 = 15

BLOCK 8

> **Record the subtraction equations for each round.**
> Optional: Draw open number lines on page 153 to help you subtract.

GAME 1

ROUND	NUMBERS ROLLED	NUMBER CHOSEN	SUBTRACTION
1			
2			
3			
4			
5			
6			
Distance from 0			

GAME 2

ROUND	NUMBERS ROLLED	NUMBER CHOSEN	SUBTRACTION
1			
2			
3			
4			
5			
6			
Distance from 0			

> Record the subtraction equations for each round.
Optional: Draw open number lines on page 153 to help you subtract.

GAME 3

ROUND	NUMBERS ROLLED	NUMBER CHOSEN	SUBTRACTION
1			
2			
3			
4			
5			
6			
Distance from 0			

GAME 4

ROUND	NUMBERS ROLLED	NUMBER CHOSEN	SUBTRACTION
1			
2			
3			
4			
5			
6			
Distance from 0			

BLOCK 8

> Optional: Use this space to record calculations or draw open number lines.

EXIT
Ticket

BLOCK
8

TOPIC 3

TOPIC 2

TOPIC 1

> **Answer this question.**

It's Round 1 and you rolled 6 and 8. What number would you make?

_____

> **Explain your reasoning.**

I would make _____ because

_____

_____

_____

_____

SCORE ⓪ ① ②

CAREER EXPLORATION

> **Accountants keep track of a company's money.**

When might accountants need to add decimals? When might they subtract them?

LESSON 5

Solve Multi-Step Problems With Decimals

> WORKED EXAMPLE

> TRY IT

> PRACTICE

Read It! Read and identify the problem.

ENTREPRENEUR

Jason makes and sells skateboards for $89.67 each. He spends $37.52 on the board and $21.03 on the wheels. How much profit does he make?

PROBLEM TYPE _____

Show It! Represent the problem.

$89.67

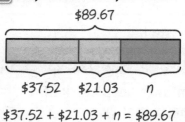

$37.52 $21.03   n

$37.52 + $21.03 + n = $89.67

Solve It! Solve the problem.

$58.55 + n = $89.67
n = $89.67 − $58.55

```
     0.45   1.00      20.00        9.00    0.67
   58.55 59.00  60.00          80.00    89.00 89.67
```

0.45 + 1.00 + 20.00 + 9.00 + 0.67 = 31.12
n = $31.12

Check It! Check your work.

1

Read It! Read and identify the problem.

FOOD TRUCK OWNER

Kim earns $52.50 from selling bagels. Lara earns $12.34 from selling muffins. If Kim gives $22.50 to Lara, how much money does Lara have now?

PROBLEM TYPE _____

Show It! Represent the problem.

Solve It! Solve the problem.

Check It! Check your work.

2

Read It! Read and identify the problem.

BUSINESS OWNER

Suri borrows $29.35 from her brother to buy office supplies. She pays some of the money back, but she still owes $13.37. How much did she pay her brother?

PROBLEM TYPE _____

Show It! Represent the problem.

Solve It! Solve the problem.

Check It! Check your work.

Why can I solve a subtraction problem by adding jumps on an open number line?

3

Nina needs to drive 78.3 mi to a client's office. She drives 24.85 mi, stops for lunch, and drives another 20.9 mi. How much farther must Nina drive?

PROBLEM TYPE _____

4

STOCKBROKER

Ed invests $912.08 in stocks and $487.78 in bonds. Then, Ed moves $378.29 from stocks to bonds. How much money does Ed now have invested in bonds?

PROBLEM TYPE _____

EXIT
Ticket

BLOCK
8

TOPIC 3

> **Solve this problem.**

Rick earns $48.75 in tips one evening. Tom earns $16.10. Then, Rick gives $13.25 to Tom. How much money does Tom have now?

PROBLEM TYPE _____

TOPIC 2

TOPIC 1

SCORE ⓪ ① ②

LESSON 1

Brain Teaser

> Arrange the numbers into factor pairs that all have the same product. Use each number once.

$\frac{1}{8}$, $\frac{1}{6}$, $\frac{1}{4}$, $\frac{1}{2}$, 6, 12, 18, 24

_____ × _____   _____ × _____

_____ × _____   _____ × _____

What is the product? _____

> **How did you solve this problem?**

I solved the problem by _____

_____

_____

_____

LESSON 2

Build It

> Use the digits to write a whole number and a decimal that have a product of 1.

| 0 | 2 | 4 | 5 |

_____ × _____ . _____ _____ = 1

> **How did you decide where to place the digits?**

I decided where to place the

digits by _____

_____

_____

LESSON 3

Which Does Not Belong?

> Estimate the product of each expression. Then circle the product that does not belong.

2 × 5.1   3 × 3.4   5 × 1.8

6 × 2.7   9 × 1.1

> **Which does not belong?**

I think that _____ does

not belong because _____

_____

_____

_____

Who's Right?

> Mary and Allie find different products for 6 × 0.12.

Mary	Allie
$6 \times 12 \times \frac{1}{100}$	$6 \times (10 + 2) \times \frac{1}{100}$
$(60 + 12) \times \frac{1}{100} = 0.72$	$(60 + 2) \times \frac{1}{100} = 0.62$

Who's right? _____

> **Explain your reasoning.**

_____ is right because

_____

_____

_____

Missing Numbers

> Find the missing digits.

$$0.2 \times 0.\underline{} = \frac{2}{\square} \times \frac{3}{\square}$$

$$= \frac{\square}{100}$$

$$= 0.0\underline{}$$

> **How did you find the missing digit in the second factor?**

The second decimal is _____

because _____

_____

_____

> In this Topic, you learned to multiply decimals by whole numbers and by other decimals.

I calculated 3.2 times 3.2 to be 1.024. But that doesn't match my estimate of 9.

Rename the decimals as fractions and then multiply.

$$3.2 \times 3.2$$
$$\frac{32}{10} \times \frac{32}{10}$$
$$(30 + 2) \times (30 + 2)$$
$$(30 \times 30) + (30 \times 2) + (2 \times 30) + (2 \times 2)$$
$$900 \quad + \quad 60 \quad + \quad 60 \quad + \quad 4 = 1024$$

$$\frac{32}{10} \times \frac{32}{10} = \frac{1024}{100}$$
$$= 10.24$$

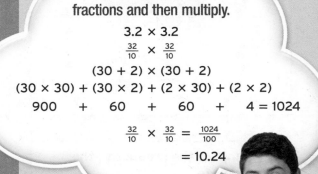

LESSON 1
CONCEPT

Multiply Decimals by Whole Numbers

> WORKED EXAMPLE

STEP 1 Make an estimate.

$$3 \times 0.24$$

Estimate: ___< 3___

STEP 2 Rename the decimal as a fraction.

Rename: $3 \times \frac{24}{100}$

STEP 3 Find the product.

Rename: $3 \times \frac{24}{100}$

$3 \times 24 \times \frac{1}{100}$

$72 \times \frac{1}{100} = \frac{72}{100}$

$72 \times \frac{1}{100} = 0.72$

STEP 4 Compare the product to the estimate.

$$3 \times 0.24 = \underline{0.72}$$

Is your answer reasonable? ___yes___

> TRY IT

1

STEP 1 Make an estimate.

$$8 \times 0.15$$

Estimate: _____

STEP 2 Rename the decimal as a fraction.

Rename:

STEP 3 Find the product.

STEP 4 Compare the product to the estimate.

$$8 \times 0.15 = \underline{\hspace{1cm}}$$

Is your answer reasonable? _____

> PRACTICE

2

STEP 1 Make an estimate.

$$4 \times 0.44$$

Estimate: _____

STEP 2 Rename the decimal as a fraction.

Rename:

STEP 3 Find the product.

STEP 4 Compare the product to the estimate.

$$4 \times 0.44 = \underline{\hspace{1cm}}$$

Is your answer reasonable? _____

BLOCK 8

3

7 × 0.21

Estimate: _____

Rename:

7 × 0.21 = _____

Is your answer reasonable? _____

4

6 × 0.32

Estimate: _____

Rename:

6 × 0.32 = _____

Is your answer reasonable? _____

> **Find the product.**

2 × 0.83

Estimate: _____

TOPIC 3

TOPIC 2

2 × 0.83 = _____

Is your answer reasonable? _____

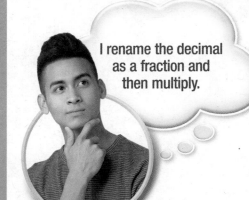

I rename the decimal as a fraction and then multiply.

TOPIC 1

SCORE ⓪ ① ②

LESSON 2
GAME

Develop Decimal Estimation Strategies

RULES

Decimal Dare (Level 2)

If one factor is a decimal less than 1, the product is less than the other factor.

What You Need
- *mSpace* pages 160–163
- decahedron (black, 0-9)

How to Play
- Players take turns.
- The target range is between 10 and 12.
- Players score a point for each attempt at getting a product in the target range.

How to Win
- The winner is the player with the fewest points after 6 attempts.

> HOW TO PLAY

BLOCK 8

STEP 1 Roll the decahedron two times.

STEP 2 Use the two numbers to make a whole number.

| GAME 1 | | | |
ATTEMPT	FACTOR 1	FACTOR 2	PRODUCT
1	36		

STEP 3 Multiply the whole number by any decimal.

$$36 \times 0.4 = 36 \times \frac{4}{10}$$

$$= \frac{144}{10}$$

$$= 14.4$$

| GAME 1 | | | |
ATTEMPT	FACTOR 1	FACTOR 2	PRODUCT
1	36	0.4	14.4

STEP 4 Multiply the whole number by another decimal until you get a product in the target range.

| GAME 1 | | | |
ATTEMPT	FACTOR 1	FACTOR 2	PRODUCT
1	36	0.4	14.4
2	36	0.2	7.2
3	36	0.3	10.8

MY TOTAL POINTS
3

RECORDING SHEET

Decimal Dare (Level 2)

> Record your factors and products.
> Optional: Use the space on page 163 to record calculations.

GAME 1

ATTEMPT	FACTOR 1	FACTOR 2	PRODUCT
1			
2			
3			
4			
5			
6			MY TOTAL POINTS

GAME 2

ATTEMPT	FACTOR 1	FACTOR 2	PRODUCT
1			
2			
3			
4			
5			
6			MY TOTAL POINTS

RECORDING SHEET
Decimal Dare (Level 2)

> Record your factors and products.
Optional: Use the space on page 163 to record calculations.

GAME 3

ATTEMPT	FACTOR 1	FACTOR 2	PRODUCT
1			
2			
3			
4			
5			
6			MY TOTAL POINTS

GAME 4

ATTEMPT	FACTOR 1	FACTOR 2	PRODUCT
1			
2			
3			
4			
5			
6			MY TOTAL POINTS

BLOCK 8

> **Optional: Use this space to record calculations.**

> **Answer this question.**

Your whole number is 22. What decimal do you choose to make a product between 10 and 12?

_____ . _____ _____

> **Explain why you chose that number.**

I chose _____ because _____

_____

_____

SCORE ⓪ ① ②

TOPIC 2

CAREER EXPLORATION

> **Real estate agents help people buy and sell houses.**

Why might a real estate agent need to multiply with decimals?

TOPIC 1

> WORKED EXAMPLE

> TRY IT

> PRACTICE

Worked Example

STEP 1 Make an estimate.

$$0.6 \times 0.35$$

Estimate: ___< 0.35___

STEP 2 Rename the decimal factors as fractions.

$$\frac{6}{10} \times \frac{35}{100}$$

STEP 3 Find the product.

$$(6 \times 30) + (6 \times 5)$$

$$180 \quad + \quad 30 \quad = 210$$

$$\frac{6}{10} \times \frac{35}{100} = \frac{210}{1000}$$

STEP 4 Rename the product.

$$\frac{210}{1000} = 0.210$$

$$0.6 \times 0.35 = \underline{\quad 0.210 \text{ or } 0.21 \quad}$$

Is your answer reasonable? ___yes___

1 Try It

STEP 1 Make an estimate.

$$0.5 \times 0.67$$

Estimate: _____

STEP 2 Rename the decimal factors as fractions.

STEP 3 Find the product.

STEP 4 Rename the product.

$$0.5 \times 0.67 = \underline{\quad\quad}$$

Is your answer reasonable? _____

2 Practice

STEP 1 Make an estimate.

$$0.8 \times 0.38$$

Estimate: _____

STEP 2 Rename the decimal factors as fractions.

STEP 3 Find the product.

STEP 4 Rename the product.

$$0.8 \times 0.38 = \underline{\quad\quad}$$

Is your answer reasonable? _____

> PRACTICE

3

0.7 × 0.71

Estimate: _____

0.7 × 0.71 = _____

Is your answer reasonable? _____

4

0.9 × 0.57

Estimate: _____

0.9 × 0.57 = _____

Is your answer reasonable? _____

BLOCK **8**

TOPIC 3

> **Find the product.**

0.5 × 0.82

Estimate: _____

TOPIC 2

0.5 × 0.82 = _____

Is your answer reasonable? _____

> **How do you know your answer is reasonable?**

I know my answer is reasonable

because _____

TOPIC 1

_____

_____

_____

_____

SCORE ⓪ ① ②

Decimal Multiplication **165**

Multiply Decimals Greater Than 1

> WORKED EXAMPLE

> TRY IT

> PRACTICE

STEP 1 Make an estimate.

$$3.7 \times 1.9$$

Estimate: $\underline{4 \times 2 = 8}$

STEP 2 Rename the decimal factors as fractions.

$$\frac{37}{10} \times \frac{19}{10}$$

STEP 3 Find the product.

$$(30 + 7) \times (10 + 9)$$
$$(30 \times 10) + (30 \times 9) + (7 \times 10) + (7 \times 9)$$
$$300 \ + \ 270 \ + \ 70 \ + \ 63 \ = 703$$

$$\frac{37}{10} \times \frac{19}{10} = \frac{703}{100}$$

STEP 4 Rename the product.

$$\frac{703}{100} = 7.03$$

$$3.7 \times 1.9 = \underline{7.03}$$

Is your answer reasonable? $\underline{yes}$

1

STEP 1 Make an estimate.

$$4.9 \times 3.1$$

Estimate: _____

STEP 2 Rename the decimal factors as fractions.

STEP 3 Find the product.

STEP 4 Rename the product.

$$4.9 \times 3.1 = \underline{\hspace{1cm}}$$

Is your answer reasonable? _____

2

STEP 1 Make an estimate.

$$6.2 \times 5.3$$

Estimate: _____

STEP 2 Rename the decimal factors as fractions.

STEP 3 Find the product.

STEP 4 Rename the product.

$$6.2 \times 5.3 = \underline{\hspace{1cm}}$$

Is your answer reasonable? _____

BLOCK 8

3

2.8 × 6.3

Estimate: _____

2.8 × 6.3 = _____

Is your answer reasonable? _____

4

6.5 × 9.7

Estimate: _____

6.5 × 9.7 = _____

Is your answer reasonable? _____

EXIT Ticket

BLOCK
8
TOPIC 3
TOPIC 2
TOPIC 1

> **Find and fix the error.**

1.9 × 4.4

$\frac{19}{10} \times \frac{44}{10}$

$(10 + 9) \times (40 + 4)$

$(10 \times 40) + (10 + 4) + (9 \times 40) + (9 \times 4)$

40 + 14 + 360 + 36 = 450

$\frac{19}{10} \times \frac{44}{10} = \frac{450}{100}$

$\frac{19}{10} \times \frac{44}{10} = 4.50$

1.9 × 4.4 = __4.50__

> **What is the first error in the solution?**

The first error in the solution is

that _____

_____

_____

_____

_____

SCORE ⓪ ① ②

LESSON 5
PROBLEM SOLVING

Identify a Rule With Decimals

> WORKED EXAMPLE

> TRY IT

> PRACTICE

STEP 1 Find the rule.

INPUT	EQUATIONS	OUTPUT
0.1		1.01
0.2		1.02
0.3		1.03
0.4		1.04
0.5	$(0.5 \times 0.1) + 1 = 1.05$	1.05

Output = $\underline{(Input \times 0.1) + 1}$

STEP 2 Express the rule with a variable.

Output = $\underline{(n \times 0.1) + 1}$

STEP 3 Complete the missing outputs.

INPUT	EQUATIONS	OUTPUT
0.1		1.01
0.2		1.02
0.3	$(0.3 \times 0.1) + 1 = 1.03$	1.03
0.4	$(0.4 \times 0.1) + 1 = 1.04$	1.04
0.5	$(0.5 \times 0.1) + 1 = 1.05$	1.05
0.8	$(0.8 \times 0.1) + 1 = 1.08$	1.08
1	$(1 \times 0.1) + 1 = 1.1$	1.1

Output = $\underline{(Input \times 0.1) + 1}$

Output = $\underline{(n \times 0.1) + 1}$

STEP 4 Apply the rule using a different input.

If the input is 100, then the output is __11__ .

1

STEP 1 Find the rule.

INPUT	EQUATIONS	OUTPUT
0.1		0.3
0.2		0.5
0.3		0.7
0.4		0.9
0.5		1.1

Output = _____

STEP 2 Express the rule with a variable.

Output = _____

STEP 3 Complete the missing outputs.

INPUT	EQUATIONS	OUTPUT
0.1		0.3
0.2		0.5
0.3		0.7
0.4		0.9
0.5		1.1
1		
2		

STEP 4 Apply the rule using a different input.

If the input is 100, then the

output is _____ .

2

STEP 1 Find the rule.

INPUT	EQUATIONS	OUTPUT
0.1		3.02
0.2		3.04
0.3		3.06
0.4		3.08
0.5		3.10

Output = _____

STEP 2 Express the rule with a variable.

Output = _____

STEP 3 Complete the missing outputs.

INPUT	EQUATIONS	OUTPUT
0.1		3.02
0.2		3.04
0.3		3.06
0.4		3.08
0.5		3.10
0.8		
1		

STEP 4 Apply the rule using a different input.

If the input is 100, then the

output is _____ .

BLOCK 8

3

STEP 1 Find the rule.

INPUT	EQUATIONS	OUTPUT
0.1		2.01
0.2		2.02
0.3		2.03
0.4		2.04
0.5		2.05

Output = _____

STEP 2 Express the rule with a variable.

Output = _____

STEP 3 Complete the missing outputs.

INPUT	EQUATIONS	OUTPUT
0.1		2.01
0.2		2.02
0.3		2.03
0.4		2.04
0.5		2.05
1		
2		

STEP 4 Apply the rule using a different input.

If the input is 100, then the

output is _____.

4

STEP 1 Find the rule.

INPUT	EQUATIONS	OUTPUT
0.1		1.05
0.2		1.10
0.3		1.15
0.4		1.20
0.5		1.25

Output = _____

STEP 2 Express the rule with a variable.

Output = _____

STEP 3 Complete the missing outputs.

INPUT	EQUATIONS	OUTPUT
0.1		1.05
0.2		1.10
0.3		1.15
0.4		1.20
0.5		1.25
1		
2		

STEP 4 Apply the rule using a different input.

If the input is 100, then the

output is _____.

EXIT Ticket

BLOCK 8

> Complete this function table.

INPUT	EQUATIONS	OUTPUT
0.1		0.25
0.2		0.45
0.3		0.65
0.4		0.85
0.5		
0.6		

For every input n, the value of

the output is _____.

If the input is 10, then the

output is _____.

Many rules could apply to a single row of a function table. But only one rule should apply to all of the rows.

TOPIC 3

TOPIC 2

TOPIC 1

LESSON 1

Build It

› Write numbers or expressions that are equivalent to 0.23.

• _____
• _____

• _____
• _____

• _____
• _____

› **What is a real-life example of the decimal number 0.23?**

A real-life example of the decimal

number 0.23 is _____

_____

LESSON 2

Missing Numbers

› Use the digits 1 to 9 to complete as many equations as you can.

$6 \div \dfrac{1}{\boxed{}} = 12$ $9 \times \dfrac{1}{\boxed{}} = 1$ $\boxed{} \div 6 = \dfrac{5}{6}$

$4 \times \dfrac{\boxed{}}{2} = 16$ $7 \times \dfrac{\boxed{}}{7} = 1$ $\boxed{} \div 8 = \dfrac{1}{2}$

$2 \times \dfrac{9}{\boxed{}} = 6$ $\dfrac{\boxed{}}{3} = 2$ $\boxed{} \div 4 = 1\dfrac{3}{4}$

› **How is a fraction the same as division?**

A fraction is the same as division

because _____

_____

LESSON 3

Find the Pattern

› Write another expression that belongs inside the circle.

0.03×10 $1.8 \div 0.6$ $1.2 \div 0.3$

$0.9 \div 0.3$

$0.12 \div 0.04$

_____

6×2 2.5×3.2

› **What do the expressions inside the circle have in common?**

The expressions inside the circle

are _____

_____

Build It

›Arrange the four digits to complete the equation.

| 0 | 2 | 4 | 6 |

___ . ___ ÷ ___ . ___ = 7

> How did you know where to place the digits?

I knew where to place the digits

because _____

_____

_____

Who's Right?

›James and Anna worked out two different answers to the same problem.

James	Anna
$1.8 ÷ 0.06 = 0.3$	$1.8 ÷ 0.06 = 30$

Who's right? _____

> How do you know who is correct?

_____ is correct because

_____

_____

_____

> In this Topic, you learned strategies for dividing decimals. Estimating the quotient helps you decide if your answer is reasonable.

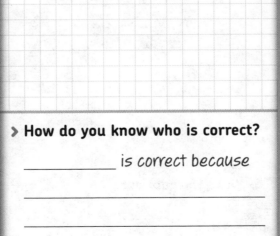

How can I divide two decimals, like 4.5 and 0.9?

Rename both decimals as fractions. They have the same denominator, so the quotient is $45 ÷ 9$.

$$\frac{45}{10} ÷ \frac{9}{10}$$

$$45 ÷ 9 = 5$$

$$4.5 ÷ 0.9 = 5$$

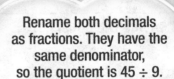

Use Models to Divide Decimals

> WORKED EXAMPLE

> TRY IT

> PRACTICE

STEP 1 Use decimal grids to divide.

$$2 \div 0.2$$

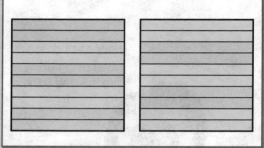

STEP 2 Rename the dividend and divisor as fractions.

$$\frac{20}{10} \div \frac{2}{10}$$

STEP 3 Divide the equal parts.

$$20 \div 2 = 10$$

STEP 4 Write the quotient.

$$2 \div 0.2 = \underline{10}$$

1

STEP 1 Rename the dividend and divisor as fractions.

$$4.5 \div 0.3$$

STEP 2 Divide the equal parts.

STEP 3 Write the quotient.

$$4.5 \div 0.3 = \underline{}$$

2

STEP 1 Rename the dividend and divisor as fractions.

$$2 \div 0.4$$

STEP 2 Divide the equal parts.

STEP 3 Write the quotient.

$$2 \div 0.4 = \underline{}$$

BLOCK 8

common denominator (n) the denominator of two or more fractions that have the same denominator

> PRACTICE

3
$$2 \div 0.1$$

4
$$4 \div 0.5$$

5
$$5 \div 0.2$$

6
$$6 \div 0.3$$

7
$$3.6 \div 0.3$$

8
$$3.9 \div 0.3$$

> Find the quotient.

$$3 \div 0.6$$

TOPIC 3

TOPIC 2

> **How can you check your answer to make sure it is correct?**

I can check my answer by

_____

_____

TOPIC 1

_____

_____

_____

_____

SCORE ⓪ ① ②

Use Patterns to Divide Decimals

STEP 1 Find a pattern in division.

DIVISION EQUATION	PLACE VALUE EQUATION	FRACTION
8 ÷ 2 = 4	(8 × 1) ÷ (2 × 1) = 4	
80 ÷ 20 = 4	(8 × 10) ÷ (2 × 10) = 4	

STEP 2 Use the pattern to find a rule.

DIVISION EQUATION	PLACE VALUE EQUATION	FRACTION
8 ÷ 2 = 4	(8 × 1) ÷ (2 × 1) = 4	$\frac{8}{2} = 4$
80 ÷ 20 = 4	(8 × 10) ÷ (2 × 10) = 4	$\frac{80}{20} = 4$
8000 ÷ 2000 = 4		$\frac{8000}{2000} = 4$

Rule: If I multiply the numerator and denominator by the
same _factor_, the value of the fraction stays
the _same_.

STEP 3 Use the rule to divide decimals.

$$0.8 ÷ 0.2$$

$$\frac{0.8 \times 10}{0.2 \times 10} = \frac{8}{2}$$

STEP 4 Find the quotient.

$$\frac{8}{2} = 4$$

$$0.8 ÷ 0.2 = \underline{\ 4\ }$$

1

STEP 1 Rename the division problem as a fraction.

$$2.4 ÷ 0.12$$

STEP 2 Find an equivalent fraction.

STEP 3 Find the quotient.

$$2.4 ÷ 0.12 = \underline{\hspace{1cm}}$$

2

STEP 1 Rename the division problem as a fraction.

$$0.4 ÷ 0.02$$

STEP 2 Find an equivalent fraction.

STEP 3 Find the quotient.

$$0.4 ÷ 0.02 = \underline{\hspace{1cm}}$$

BLOCK 8

3	2.4 ÷ 0.8

4	3.6 ÷ 0.6

5	0.12 ÷ 0.06

6	1.8 ÷ 0.02

7	0.81 ÷ 0.009

8	48 ÷ 0.8

EXIT Ticket

BLOCK 8

> **Find the quotient.**

$$0.24 ÷ 0.004$$

TOPIC 3

TOPIC 2

> **The divisor 0.004 is almost zero. What does this tell you about the quotient?**

The divisor 0.004 tells me that

_____

_____

TOPIC 1

_____

_____

_____

_____

SCORE ⓪ ① ②

Patterns in Decimal Division **175**

LESSON 3
CONCEPT

Divide Decimals

> WORKED EXAMPLE   > TRY IT   > PRACTICE

STEP 1 Estimate the quotient.

$$0.3 \div 1.5$$

Estimate: < 0.3

STEP 2 Write the quotient as a fraction.

Rename: $\dfrac{0.3}{1.5} \times \dfrac{10}{10} = \dfrac{3}{15}$

STEP 3 Rename the fraction as a decimal.

$$\dfrac{3}{15} \div \dfrac{3}{3} = \dfrac{1}{5}$$

$$\dfrac{1}{5} \times \dfrac{2}{2} = \dfrac{2}{10} \text{ or } 0.2$$

STEP 4 Compare the quotient to the estimate.

$$0.3 \div 1.5 = \underline{0.2}$$

Is your answer reasonable? $\underline{yes}$

1

STEP 1 Estimate the quotient.

$$1.5 \div 0.8$$

Estimate: _____

STEP 2 Write the quotient as a fraction.

STEP 3 Rename the fraction as a decimal.

STEP 4 Compare the quotient to the estimate.

$$1.5 \div 0.8 = \underline{\hspace{1cm}}$$

Is your answer reasonable? _____

2

STEP 1 Estimate the quotient.

$$6.03 \div 0.12$$

Estimate: _____

STEP 2 Write the quotient as a fraction.

STEP 3 Rename the fraction as a decimal.

STEP 4 Compare the quotient to the estimate.

$$6.03 \div 0.12 = \underline{\hspace{1cm}}$$

Is your answer reasonable? _____

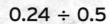

I always estimate the quotient before dividing so I can make sure my answer is reasonable.

3

0.24 ÷ 0.5

4

5.5 ÷ 2.2

5

10.75 ÷ 0.5

6

12.25 ÷ 2.5

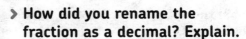

EXIT Ticket

BLOCK 8

> **Find the quotient.**

3.5 ÷ 0.4

TOPIC 3

TOPIC 2

> **How did you rename the fraction as a decimal? Explain.**

I renamed _____ by _____

_____

_____ because _____

TOPIC 1

_____

_____

_____

_____

_____

SCORE ⓪ ① ②

Estimating the quotients helps me decide whether to use a number as tenths or hundredths.

RULES
Decimal Dare (Level 3)

What You Need
- *mSpace* pages 178–181
- spinner

How to Play
- Players take turns.
- The quotient is the score for each round.

How to Win
- After 6 rounds, the winner is the player whose score is closest to 50 without going over.
- If one player's score goes over 50, the other player wins.

> HOW TO PLAY

STEP 1 Spin the spinner two times.

STEP 2 Use one number as tenths and the other as hundredths.

GAME 1		
SPIN NUMBERS	RECORD NUMBERS AS TENTHS AND HUNDREDTHS	QUOTIENT
4 8	0. _8_ ÷ 0.0 _4_	
	0. ___ ÷ 0.0	

STEP 3 Divide tenths by hundredths and record the quotient.

GAME 1			
SPIN NUMBERS	RECORD NUMBERS AS TENTHS AND HUNDREDTHS	QUOTIENT	SCORE
4 8	0. _8_ ÷ 0.0 _4_ $\frac{80}{100} \div \frac{4}{100} = 20$	20	20
	0. ___ ÷ 0.0		

STEP 4 Add the quotient to the previous quotient.

GAME 1			
SPIN NUMBERS	RECORD NUMBERS AS TENTHS AND HUNDREDTHS	QUOTIENT	SCORE
4 8	0. _8_ ÷ 0.0 _4_ $\frac{80}{100} \div \frac{4}{100} = 20$	20	20
1 2	0. _1_ ÷ 0.0 _2_ $\frac{10}{100} \div \frac{2}{100} = 5$	5	25

BLOCK 8

RECORDING SHEET

Decimal Dare (Level 3)

> Record your spins and equations.
> Optional: Use the grid paper on page 181 to record calculations.

GAME 1

SPIN NUMBERS	RECORD NUMBERS AS TENTHS AND HUNDREDTHS	QUOTIENT	SCORE
	0. _____ ÷ 0.0 _____		
	0. _____ ÷ 0.0 _____		
	0. _____ ÷ 0.0 _____		
	0. _____ ÷ 0.0 _____		
	0. _____ ÷ 0.0 _____		
	0. _____ ÷ 0.0 _____		**TOTAL SCORE**

GAME 2

SPIN NUMBERS	RECORD NUMBERS AS TENTHS AND HUNDREDTHS	QUOTIENT	SCORE
	0. _____ ÷ 0.0 _____		
	0. _____ ÷ 0.0 _____		
	0. _____ ÷ 0.0 _____		
	0. _____ ÷ 0.0 _____		
	0. _____ ÷ 0.0 _____		
	0. _____ ÷ 0.0 _____		**TOTAL SCORE**

RECORDING SHEET

Decimal Dare (Level 3)

> Record your spins and equations.
> Optional: Use the grid paper on page 181 to record calculations.

GAME 3

SPIN NUMBERS	RECORD NUMBERS AS TENTHS AND HUNDREDTHS	QUOTIENT	SCORE
	0. _____ ÷ 0.0 _____		
	0. _____ ÷ 0.0 _____		
	0. _____ ÷ 0.0 _____		
	0. _____ ÷ 0.0 _____		
	0. _____ ÷ 0.0 _____		
	0. _____ ÷ 0.0 _____		TOTAL SCORE

GAME 4

SPIN NUMBERS	RECORD NUMBERS AS TENTHS AND HUNDREDTHS	QUOTIENT	SCORE
	0. _____ ÷ 0.0 _____		
	0. _____ ÷ 0.0 _____		
	0. _____ ÷ 0.0 _____		
	0. _____ ÷ 0.0 _____		
	0. _____ ÷ 0.0 _____		
	0. _____ ÷ 0.0 _____		TOTAL SCORE

> **Optional:** Use this space to record calculations.

> **Answer this question.**

Your score is 45. You spin a 1 and a 4. Which numbers would you use for tenths and hundredths?

_____ tenths ÷ _____ hundredths

> **Why did you make this choice?**

I used _____ as tenths and

_____ as hundredths because

_____

_____

_____

SCORE ⓪ ① ②

TOPIC 3

TOPIC 2

TOPIC 1

CAREER EXPLORATION

> **Financial advisors help people save and invest their money.**

How could a financial advisor use division to help clients plan where to invest their money?

LESSON 5
PROBLEM SOLVING

Solve Equal Groups Problems With Decimals

> **WORKED EXAMPLE**　　　　> **TRY IT**　　　　> **PRACTICE**

Read It! Read and identify the problem.

 **ENTREPRENEUR** Today, $\frac{3}{4}$ of Ken's earnings came from selling apps for $0.48 each. All his other sales earned him $0.96. How many apps did Ken sell?

PROBLEM TYPE _____

Show It! Represent the problem.

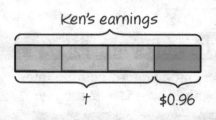

Ken's earnings

t　　　$0.96

Solve It! Solve the problem.

$t = 3 \times \$0.96$　　　　$n = \$2.88 \div \$0.48$

$\quad = 3 \times \frac{96}{100}$　　　　$\quad = \frac{288}{100} \div \frac{48}{100}$

$\quad = \frac{288}{100}$　　　　$\quad = \frac{288}{48}$

$\quad = \$2.88$　　　　$\quad = 6$

Check It! Check your work.

1

Read It! Read and identify the problem.

 FOOD SERVICE MANAGER Emily buys food for an office party. After spending $\frac{4}{5}$ of her money on tacos, she has $6.04 left. One taco costs $3.02. How many tacos did she buy?

PROBLEM TYPE _____

Show It! Represent the problem.

Solve It! Solve the problem.

Check It! Check your work.

2

Read It! Read and identify the problem.

 **REAL ESTATE AGENT** Ji spends $44 on new ads to sell a house. She spends $\frac{5}{8}$ of the money for online ads, and the rest for ads in print. Each print ad costs $3.30. How many print ads does she buy?

PROBLEM TYPE _____

Show It! Represent the problem.

Solve It! Solve the problem.

Check It! Check your work.

I can draw bar models with equal parts to help me understand the information in the problems.

3

ACCOUNTANT

Ed receives a tax refund of $37.50. He spends $\frac{2}{3}$ of his refund on clothing. He divides the rest among his 5 children. How much money does he give each child?

PROBLEM TYPE _____

4

FINANCIAL ADVISOR

Sue earns a $97.50 bonus. Her financial advisor has her save $\frac{3}{10}$ of it. Sue buys concert tickets that cost $22.75 each using the rest of her bonus. How many can she buy?

PROBLEM TYPE _____

EXIT Ticket

> **Solve this problem.**

Myra spends $68.24 on movies. She spends $\frac{1}{4}$ of the money buying movies online, and the rest on DVDs. If each DVD costs $17.06, how many DVDs does Myra buy?

BLOCK **8**

TOPIC 3

TOPIC 2

TOPIC 1

SCORE ⓪ ① ②

> **YOUR JOB**
Entrepreneur

> **YOUR TASK**
Create two schedules, calculate wages, and then choose the better schedule for your business.

ANCHOR VIDEO CONNECTION

As the Anchor Video shows, business owners need to satisfy their customers to earn a profit.

Manage a Tutoring Business

> Your tutoring business offers 13 sessions on computer skills every Saturday. Create a schedule to satisfy both the customers and tutors.

A EXPLORE

Complete two sample schedules by writing the tutors' names in the blank spaces. You may assign a tutor to any subject, but each tutor prefers his or her strength. A tutor's sessions must not overlap.

Name	Ken	Pilar	Tariq	Val
Rate (per hour)	$10.80	$ 11.00	$ 9.60	$ 11.40
Strength	Databases	Web design	Smart phones	Blogging
Available Hours	9A.M.–12 noon	8A.M.–12 noon	8A.M.–12 noon	8A.M.–11:30A.M.

▢ 0.5 hr   ▢ 0.75 hr   ▢ 1.25 hr

	8:00	8:30	9:00	9:30	10:00	10:30	11:00	11:30	12:00

SCHEDULE A

Databases

Web design

Blogging

Smart phones

SCHEDULE B

Databases

Web design

Blogging

Smart phones

For each schedule, complete the table to find each tutor's wages and the total wages for the Saturday sessions.

SCHEDULE A

TUTOR	TOTAL HOURS	HOURLY RATE	WAGES
Ken	(× 0.5) + (× 0.75) + (× 1.25) =	$10.80	
Pilar	(× 0.5) + (× 0.75) + (× 1.25) =	$11.00	
Tariq	(× 0.5) + (× 0.75) + (× 1.25) =	$ 9.60	
Val	(× 0.5) + (× 0.75) + (× 1.25) =	$11.40	
TOTAL			

SCHEDULE B

TUTOR	TOTAL HOURS	HOURLY RATE	WAGES
Ken	(× 0.5) + (× 0.75) + (× 1.25) =	$10.80	
Pilar	(× 0.5) + (× 0.75) + (× 1.25) =	$11.00	
Tariq	(× 0.5) + (× 0.75) + (× 1.25) =	$ 9.60	
Val	(× 0.5) + (× 0.75) + (× 1.25) =	$11.40	
TOTAL			

C ANALYZE

INTERPRET Could you complete the schedule if tutors teach only their strongest subjects? Why or why not?

_____

_____

REFLECT Which of the two schedules would you choose? Explain your decision.

_____

_____

Evaluate

> Rate how well you and your partner understood and completed each part of the performance task:

Rating Scale			
None	Limited	Partial	Thorough
0	1	2	3

A Completed two schedules.

Me	0	1	2	3
Partner	0	1	2	3

B Completed two tables to calculate hours and wages.

Me	0	1	2	3
Partner	0	1	2	3

C Answered each question reasonably and accurately.

Me	0	1	2	3
Partner	0	1	2	3

EXTEND

You want to hire a fifth tutor. What should be this tutor's strength? Use another sheet of paper to prepare a new schedule for the five tutors.

Reflect on Your Learning Attitudes

Congratulations! You've completed Block 8 of *MATH 180*.
Respond to these questions by checking EACH sentence
that describes your mindset.

A GETTING FOCUSED

These strategies help you have a clear focus and plan to meet the challenges of learning difficult mathematics.

How did you prepare for new math lessons in BLOCK 8 ?

- [ ] I set a clear and challenging goal for myself to learn the math content.
- [ ] I made a schedule or chose certain times for studying math.
- [ ] I made plans to study math with a classmate, friend, or family member.
- [ ] I reviewed earlier lessons, especially if I was unsure about their content.
- [ ] If I had been distracted while studying math in the past, I took steps to avoid the distractions this time.

- [ ] Other *(please describe)*:
  _____
  _____
  _____
  _____
  _____
  _____

B DEVELOPING YOUR BRAIN

These strategies help new connections develop in your brain, allowing you to think in new ways and learn new knowledge.

What steps did you take as you solved BLOCK 8 math problems?

- [ ] I broke down a complex problem into simpler parts or steps.
- [ ] I related or compared a new problem to a problem I had solved before.
- [ ] I wrote all of the important steps of the solution, and I drew pictures or constructed diagrams or charts when they were useful.
- [ ] I used the glossary to learn math terms.
- [ ] I reviewed the solutions to the Worked Example and Try It problems in the *mSpace* before I started working on the Practice problems.

- [ ] Other *(please describe)*:
  _____
  _____
  _____
  _____
  _____
  _____

C KEEPING POSITIVE

Negative emotions can make learning difficult or impossible. These strategies keep your brain ready to learn.

How did you keep your mood and motivation positive during BLOCK 8 ?

- [ ] I practiced thinking positive instead of negative thoughts.
- [ ] I imagined that new connections were developing in my brain.
- [ ] I reminded myself that I could learn from mistakes.
- [ ] I chose to work with classmates who have positive attitudes and who help me learn.
- [ ] I practiced calming strategies and took study breaks when I needed them.

- [ ] Other *(please describe)*:
  _____
  _____
  _____
  _____
  _____

Score Your Mindset

> **Count up all your checks and write the total here:**

If you checked . . .	You were in the following zone, which means . . .
 **Less than 3**	**Fixed Mindset Zone** You didn't use many brain-wise learning strategies this time. Your mindset may have held you back from doing your best.
3-5	**Mixed Mindset Zone** You used some good strategies but skipped some others. Your mindset may have kept you from doing your best work.
6 or more	**Growth Mindset Zone** Overall, your use of learning strategies was in the Growth Mindset Zone this time. You used lots of good strategies that will help you grow your brain and get smarter.

> **How can you develop a Growth Mindset?**

- Read the list of strategies in the Mindset Scan again.
- Choose one strategy from each category that you think would help you learn. Copy these strategies into a journal or notebook.
- Remind yourself about the strategies as you are studying the next Block.

Brain Boosting

> **What will you do to help your brain stay in the Growth Mindset Zone?**

I will focus on:

- ☐ Setting the stage and focusing attention
- ☐ Growing new brain connections
- ☐ Keeping a positive mood and motivation

 Anything is possible if you've got enough nerve.

J. K. Rowling
Best-selling author

What will I do?

_____
_____
_____
_____
_____

Who will help me?

_____
_____
_____
_____
_____

When will I do it?

_____
_____
_____
_____

How will this help me to grow?

_____
_____
_____
_____

VOCABULARY

- additive inverse
- benchmark number
- integer
- negative
- number line
- operation
- opposite
- positive

Living Below Zero

Could you live in a place with extreme temperatures?

In this Anchor Video, Antarctica's extreme temperatures are a daily challenge for the scientists who work there.

Math in the Environment

In this Block, you will explore how math is used in the environmental sciences.

ENVIRONMENTAL Engineers

use science to **solve complex problems**, such as how to best protect water supplies and combat air pollution.

MARINE Geologists

explore the oceans, which cover more than $\frac{2}{3}$ of Earth's surface. The deepest part of the ocean is **36,200 feet** or **11,030 meters** deep.

WILDLIFE Biologists

use **data analysis** to study patterns of animal behavior. They work to save endangered species like the Bengal tiger—there are **fewer than 2,500** left in the wild.

Have you heard the term inner space?

Geoscientists

study Earth's features up to **3954 miles** or **6360 kilometers** inside Earth's inner core. Their research helps predict earthquakes and volcano eruptions.

COASTAL Oceanographers

study the plants, animals, and tides of the earth's **213,000 miles** or **342,790 kilometers** of coastline.

LESSON 1

Block Preview

> **Think about the Anchor Video and answer this question.**

If you were a scientist living and working in Antarctica, what would you want to research?

> **Explain your thinking.**

I would want to research _____

_____

_____

LESSON 2

Which Does Not Belong?

> **These numbers have something in common. Circle a number that does not belong.**

−16, 8, −2, −4, −6, −5

> **Is there another number that does not belong for a different reason? Explain why.**

_____ does not belong because

_____

_____

LESSON 3

Brain Teaser

> **Solve this riddle.**

Draw a number line. Start at 0, go to the right 4 intervals, and then go to the left 3 intervals. Finally, go 1 interval to the left.

Where are you? _____

> **Could you solve this riddle without drawing a number line?**

I could/could not solve this riddle without drawing a number line because _____

_____

LESSON 4

Missing Numbers

> Fill in the missing numbers on the number line.

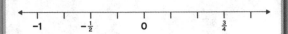

-1 $-\frac{1}{2}$ 0 $\frac{3}{4}$

> Explain your first step in solving this problem.

My first step in solving this

problem was _____

_____

_____

LESSON 5

Who's Right?

> Lee and Jenna wrote two different inequalities to compare these numbers.

$-\frac{1}{2}$ ☐ 0.42

Lee	Jenna
$-\frac{1}{2} < 0.42$	$-\frac{1}{2} > 0.42$

Who's right? _____

> Do you agree with Lee or Jenna? Defend your answer.

I agree with _____ because

_____

_____

Which is greater: −1.5 or −1.7?

I can see that −1.5 is greater than −1.7 because −1.7 is farther away from 0.

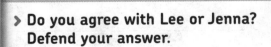

-2 -1.7 -1.5 -1 -0.5 0 0.5 1

LESSON 1
CONCEPT

Describe Situations With Integers

> WORKED EXAMPLE

> TRY IT

> PRACTICE

WORKED EXAMPLE

STEP 1 Plot positive integers on the number line.

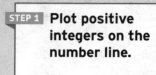

STEP 2 Plot negative integers on the number line.

Lowest Temperature	
Atlanta	−8°F
Austin	−2°F
Las Vegas	8°F
Portland	−3°F
Seattle	9°F

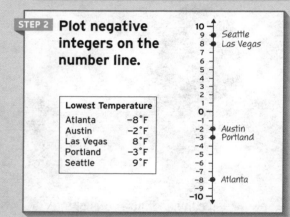

STEP 3 List cities in order of temperature from warmest to coldest.

Seattle

Las Vegas

Austin

Portland

Atlanta

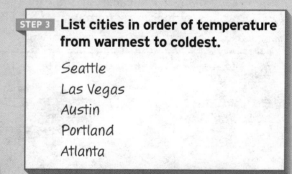

STEP 4 List integers in order from least to greatest.

−8 < −3 < −2 < 8 < 9

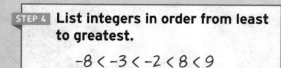

1 TRY IT

STEP 1 Plot temperatures on a number line.

Average January Temperatures	
Atlanta	1°F
Austin	5°F
Baltimore	−4°F
Cleveland	−6°F
Dallas	3°F
Memphis	0°F
Milwaukee	−9°F

STEP 2 Compare integers using a number line.

Which city is warmer in January, Baltimore or Milwaukee?

_____

STEP 3 List integers in order from least to greatest.

Temperatures from coldest to warmest:

_____

2 PRACTICE

STEP 1 Plot temperatures on a number line.

Average February Temperatures	
Austin	7°F
Baltimore	−3°F
Cleveland	−5°F
Denver	−7°F
Las Vegas	6°F
Memphis	2°F
Hartford	−6°F

STEP 2 Compare integers using a number line.

Which city is warmer in February, Denver or Hartford?

_____

STEP 3 List integers in order from least to greatest.

Temperatures from coldest to warmest:

_____

> PRACTICE

3

Plot and compare the lowest temperatures around the world.

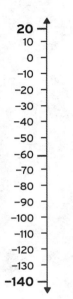

20 / 10 / 0 / −10 / −20 / −30 / −40 / −50 / −60 / −70 / −80 / −90 / −100 / −110 / −120 / −130 / **−140**

Lowest Temperatures Around the World	
Antarctica	−129°F
Greenland	−87°F
North America	−81°F
Oceania	14°F
Africa	−11°F
South America	−27°F

Which continent is warmer, Antarctica or North America?

_____

Temperatures from coldest to warmest:

_____

4

Plot and compare the average December temperatures.

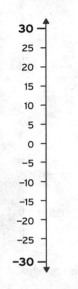

8 / 6 / 4 / 2 / 0 / −2 / −4 / −6 / −8 / −10 / −12 / **−14**

Average December Temperatures	
Charlotte	0°F
Minneapolis	−11°F
Milwaukee	−7°F
Dallas	4°F
Jacksonville	7°F
Louisville	−1°F
Denver	−9°F

Which city is warmer, Denver or Minneapolis?

_____

Temperatures from coldest to warmest:

_____

EXIT Ticket

BLOCK **9**

> Plot and compare the lowest recorded temperatures.

TOPIC 3

30 / 25 / 20 / 15 / 10 / 5 / 0 / −5 / −10 / −15 / −20 / −25 / **−30**

Lowest Recorded Temperatures of Cities	
Cincinnati	22°F
New York City	−15°F
San Francisco	27°F
Montgomery	10°F
Dallas	−1°F

Which city is warmer, New York City or Cincinnati?

_____

Temperatures from coldest to warmest:

_____

> **How do you know which city is the coldest?**

I know which city is the coldest

because _____

_____

TOPIC 2

TOPIC 1

SCORE ⓪ ① ②

LESSON 2

CONCEPT

Locate Numbers on a Number Line

> WORKED EXAMPLE

> TRY IT

> PRACTICE

STEP 1 Label a number line.

Plot 4, −2, −5.

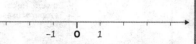

STEP 2 Plot integers.

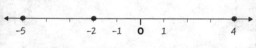

Order from least to greatest:

$$-5 < -2 < 4$$

STEP 3 Label a number line.

Plot $-\frac{1}{2}$, $\frac{1}{4}$, $-1\frac{3}{4}$, $2\frac{1}{2}$.

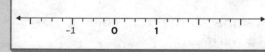

STEP 4 Plot fractions.

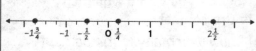

Order from least to greatest:

$$-1\frac{3}{4} < -\frac{1}{2} < \frac{1}{4} < 2\frac{1}{2}$$

1

STEP 1 Label a number line.

Plot −2, 3, −5.

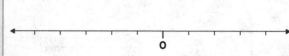

STEP 2 Plot integers.

Order from least to greatest:

_____

STEP 3 Label a number line.

Plot $-\frac{3}{4}$, $-1\frac{1}{2}$, $1\frac{1}{4}$.

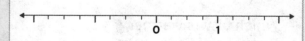

STEP 4 Plot fractions.

Order from least to greatest:

_____

2

STEP 1 Label a number line.

Plot −6, −1, 2.

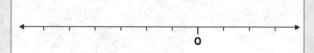

STEP 2 Plot integers.

Order from least to greatest:

_____

STEP 3 Label a number line.

Plot $-\frac{1}{2}$, $\frac{3}{2}$, $-\frac{5}{2}$.

STEP 4 Plot fractions.

Order from least to greatest:

_____

BLOCK 9

> PRACTICE

3

Plot −3, 4, −7.

Order from least to greatest:

_____

4

Plot −1, −4, −8.

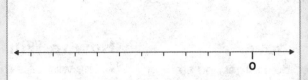

Order from least to greatest:

_____

5

Plot $-1\frac{2}{3}$, −3, $-\frac{2}{3}$.

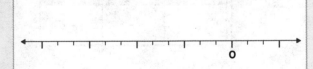

Order from least to greatest:

_____

6

Plot $-2\frac{3}{4}$, $-3\frac{1}{2}$, $-\frac{7}{4}$.

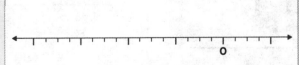

Order from least to greatest:

_____

BLOCK
9

> **Find the errors and fix the math.**

Arnie made some mistakes when he labeled these fractions on the number line.

Find his errors and fix them so the numbers are plotted correctly.

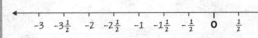

TOPIC 3

TOPIC 2

> **What errors did Arnie make?**

The errors Arnie made were

_____

_____

TOPIC 1

_____

_____

_____

_____

SCORE ⓪ ① ②

I count the intervals on the number line to check that I made my jumps correctly.

RULES
Number Jump! (Level 1)

What You Need
- *mSpace* pages 194–197
- number cube (green, 1–6)

What to Know
- Players decide if target and starting numbers are positive or negative.
- Players may jump over the target number, but not beyond the number line.
- Players record on their own number lines.

How to Win
- The winner is the first player to land on the target number.

> HOW TO PLAY

STEP 1 Roll the number cube twice. The first roll is the target number and the second roll is the starting number. Mark the target number.

TARGET NUMBER	STARTING NUMBER
–5	+4

–5 –4 –3 –2 –1 0 1 2 3 4

STEP 2 Roll the number cube again and record your number. Decide the direction of the jump.

NUMBER ROLLED	DIRECTION OF JUMP	LANDING NUMBER
6	–	

STEP 3 Jump from the starting number or the last number landed on.

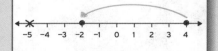

–5 –4 –3 –2 –1 0 1 2 3 4

STEP 4 Record the landing number. Trade turns.

NUMBER ROLLED	DIRECTION OF JUMP	LANDING NUMBER
6	–	–2

RECORDING SHEET

Number Jump! (Level 1)

> Record the number rolled, direction of jump, and landing number for each turn. Optional: Use the space on page 197 for calculations.

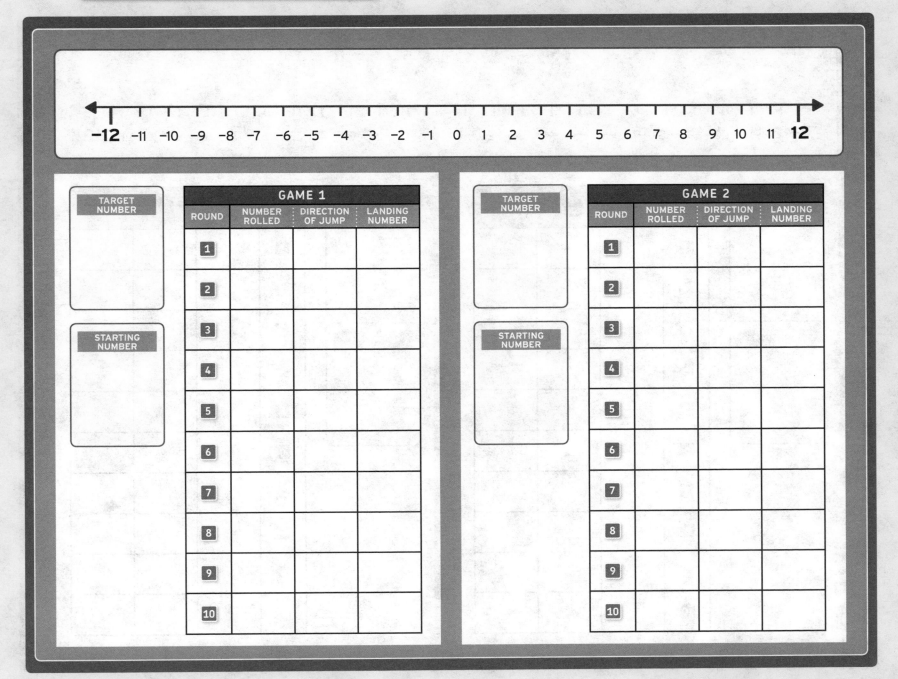

TARGET NUMBER

STARTING NUMBER

	GAME 1		
ROUND	NUMBER ROLLED	DIRECTION OF JUMP	LANDING NUMBER
1			
2			
3			
4			
5			
6			
7			
8			
9			
10			

TARGET NUMBER

STARTING NUMBER

	GAME 2		
ROUND	NUMBER ROLLED	DIRECTION OF JUMP	LANDING NUMBER
1			
2			
3			
4			
5			
6			
7			
8			
9			
10			

BLOCK 9 > TOPIC 1
LESSON 3

RECORDING SHEET
Number Jump! (Level 1)

> Record the number rolled, direction of jump, and landing number for each turn. Optional: Use the space on page 197 for calculations.

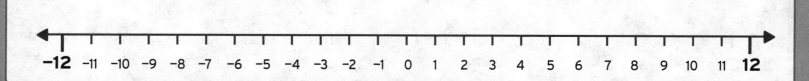

-12 -11 -10 -9 -8 -7 -6 -5 -4 -3 -2 -1 0 1 2 3 4 5 6 7 8 9 10 11 **12**

TARGET NUMBER				
STARTING NUMBER				

GAME 3			
ROUND	NUMBER ROLLED	DIRECTION OF JUMP	LANDING NUMBER
1			
2			
3			
4			
5			
6			
7			
8			
9			
10			

TARGET NUMBER				
STARTING NUMBER				

GAME 4			
ROUND	NUMBER ROLLED	DIRECTION OF JUMP	LANDING NUMBER
1			
2			
3			
4			
5			
6			
7			
8			
9			
10			

BLOCK 9

> **Optional: Use this page for calculations.**

> **Answer this question.**

You are playing *Number Jump!* You land on −3 and your target is 1. What number do you need to roll to win? Explain your reasoning.

I need to roll a _____ to win

because _____

_____

_____

_____

_____

SCORE ⓪ ① ②

CAREER EXPLORATION

> **Geoscientists study the Earth by researching its rocks and soil.**

How could a geoscientist use a number line to show how far to drill down for a soil sample?

LESSON 4
CONCEPT

Compare Positive and Negative Numbers

> WORKED EXAMPLE   > TRY IT   > PRACTICE

STEP 1 Compare positive and negative numbers.

Plot and compare
2, $-3\frac{1}{2}$, -6, -1.25.

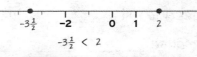

$-3\frac{1}{2} < 2$

STEP 2 Compare two negative numbers.

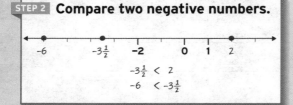

$-3\frac{1}{2} < 2$
$-6 < -3\frac{1}{2}$

STEP 3 Compare decimals to fractions.

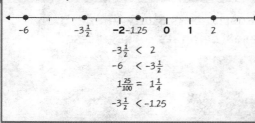

$-3\frac{1}{2} < 2$
$-6 < -3\frac{1}{2}$
$1\frac{25}{100} = 1\frac{1}{4}$
$-3\frac{1}{2} < -1.25$

STEP 4 Order numbers from least to greatest.

$-6 < -3\frac{1}{2} < -1.25 < 2$

_____

1

STEP 1 Plot integers.

Plot -3.9, 4, $-5\frac{1}{2}$, -7.

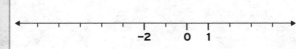

STEP 2 Plot fractions.

STEP 3 Plot decimals.

STEP 4 Order numbers from least to greatest.

_____

2

STEP 1 Plot integers.

Plot $-3\frac{1}{2}$, 2, -1.5, -6.

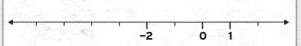

STEP 2 Plot fractions.

STEP 3 Plot decimals.

STEP 4 Order numbers from least to greatest.

_____

> PRACTICE

3

Plot $-4\frac{1}{8}$, 3, -2.5, -5.

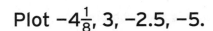

Order numbers from least to greatest:

_____

4

Plot -5.5, 1, $-3\frac{1}{4}$, -6.

Order numbers from least to greatest:

_____

5

Plot $-2\frac{7}{8}$, 2, -0.5, $\frac{7}{8}$.

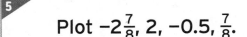

Order numbers from least to greatest:

_____

6

Plot $-\frac{24}{6}$, 2, -1.90, $-\frac{5}{2}$.

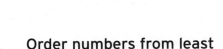

Order numbers from least to greatest:

_____

EXIT Ticket

BLOCK **9**

> **Solve this problem.**

Plot these numbers on the number line:

$$\frac{1}{2}, -4.8, -1\frac{1}{4}, -3$$

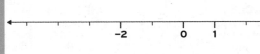

Order numbers from least to greatest:

_____

> **What two integers does −4.8 fall between?**

The two integers -4.8 falls

between are _____ and _____.

TOPIC 3

TOPIC 2

TOPIC 1

> Plotting numbers on a number line helps me visualize which numbers have greater or lesser values.

SCORE ⓪ ① ②

Rational Numbers on a Number Line **199**

LESSON 5
PROBLEM SOLVING

Sort Positive and Negative Numbers

WORKED EXAMPLE

STEP 1 Analyze the problem.

Sort these numbers:

$$-3.5, -\frac{4}{5}, 4, -\frac{1}{10}, 0.9,$$
$$3.5, -6.5, 8.1$$

CIRCLE A Numbers between −5 and 5

CIRCLE B Numbers equal to or greater than 0

STEP 2 Create a number line.

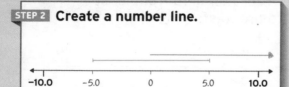

STEP 3 Plot the numbers on the number line.

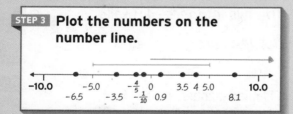

STEP 4 Complete the Venn diagram.

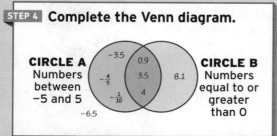

CIRCLE A Numbers between −5 and 5

CIRCLE B Numbers equal to or greater than 0

TRY IT

1

STEP 1 Analyze the problem.

Sort these numbers:

$$-2.5, -\frac{1}{4}, 2, 0.5, 3, -0.3, \frac{1}{6}$$

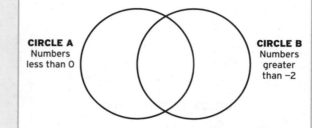

CIRCLE A Numbers less than 0

CIRCLE B Numbers greater than −2

STEP 2 Create a number line.

STEP 3 Plot the numbers on the number line.

STEP 4 Complete the Venn diagram.

PRACTICE

2

STEP 1 Analyze the problem.

Sort these numbers:

$$4, -4, \frac{1}{2}, 0.3, -\frac{3}{10}, 2, -5, -2.5$$

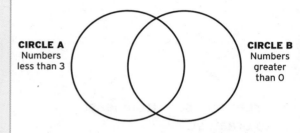

CIRCLE A Numbers less than 3

CIRCLE B Numbers greater than 0

STEP 2 Create a number line.

STEP 3 Plot the numbers on the number line.

STEP 4 Complete the Venn diagram.

3

Sort these numbers:

$-5, \frac{3}{4}, 5.2, 3, -4, -\frac{10}{3}, -4.5, 1$

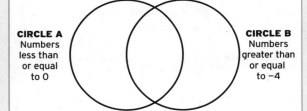

CIRCLE A
Numbers less than or equal to 0

CIRCLE B
Numbers greater than or equal to −4

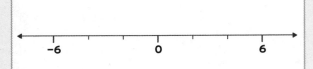

4

Sort these numbers:

$-2.1, 3, -1, 0, \frac{4}{3}, -\frac{9}{4}, -3, -0.175$

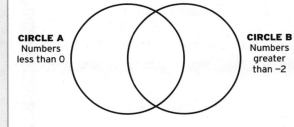

CIRCLE A
Numbers less than 0

CIRCLE B
Numbers greater than −2

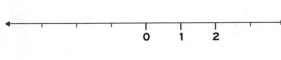

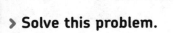

EXIT Ticket

> Solve this problem.

Sort these numbers:

$-3, 1, 7.5, -6, -\frac{3}{2}, 3\frac{1}{2}$

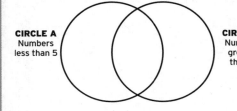

CIRCLE A
Numbers less than 5

CIRCLE B
Numbers greater than 0

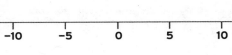

BLOCK 9

TOPIC 3

TOPIC 2

TOPIC 1

Plotting numbers on a number line helps me sort the numbers into the correct circles.

SCORE ⓪ ① ②

Build It

› Use these numbers to write addition equations with three addends.

| 2 | 3 | 5 | 6 | 8 | 13 | 19 | 21 | 24 |

- _____ • _____
- _____ • _____
- _____ • _____
- _____ • _____

› Create an equation with 4 addends. Explain how you did it.

____ + ____ + ____ + ____ = ____

I created an equation with 4

addends by _____

_____

Missing Numbers

› Fill in the blanks using these numbers to make the sentences below true. You may use a number more than once.

−5   9   −1   7   −12   4   −8

_____ is farthest from 0.

_____ is closest to 0.

_____ and _____ are farthest apart.

_____ and _____ are closest in distance.

_____ and _____ are at a distance of 5 intervals.

› How do you know which two numbers are the farthest apart?

I know which two numbers are

farthest apart because _____

_____

_____

Brain Teaser

› Complete the puzzle.

−3	+		=	−6
+	■	+	■	+
		+		=
=	■	=	■	=
−8	+	4	=	

› What was the first step you took to solve this puzzle?

My first step to solve this puzzle

was _____

_____

_____

LESSON 4

Find the Pattern

> Fill in the missing integers and find the pattern.

$$\underline{\hspace{2cm}} + 5 = -1$$
$$4 + \underline{\hspace{2cm}} = -1$$
$$(-7) + \underline{\hspace{2cm}} = -1$$
$$\underline{\hspace{2cm}} + (-10) = -1$$
$$2 + \underline{\hspace{2cm}} = -1$$
$$\underline{\hspace{2cm}} + 12 = -1$$
$$100 + \underline{\hspace{2cm}} = -1$$

> Use the pattern to write two equations with a sum of –1. Be sure that one addend is positive and the other is negative.

$$\underline{\hspace{2cm}} + \underline{\hspace{2cm}} = -1$$

$$\underline{\hspace{2cm}} + \underline{\hspace{2cm}} = -1$$

LESSON 5

Number Strings

> Add this expression. Rewrite these numbers in the order you would add them. Then write the sum.

$$35 + 17 + (-20) + (-17) + (-15)$$

> Why did you add the numbers in this order?

I added the numbers in this order

because _____

_____

_____

> In this Topic, you learned to add positive and negative numbers.

How can I add numbers with different signs, like 3 + (−5)?

First, I find the difference between 3 and 5, which is 2. I know the sum will be negative because −5 is farther from 0 than 3.

$$3 + (-5) = -2$$

LESSON 1
CONCEPT

Add Integers With the Same Sign

> WORKED EXAMPLE   > TRY IT   > PRACTICE

STEP 1 Represent two positive integers.

$$2 + 5$$

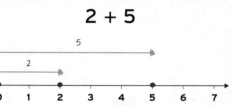

STEP 2 Find the sum.

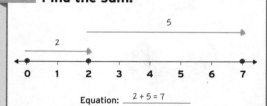

Equation: _2 + 5 = 7_

STEP 3 Represent two negative integers.

$$(-5) + (-4)$$

STEP 4 Find the sum.

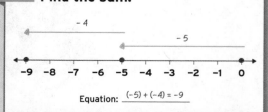

Equation: _(-5) + (-4) = -9_

1

STEP 1 Represent two positive integers.

$$3 + 6$$

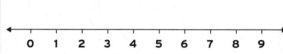

STEP 2 Find the sum.

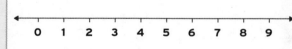

Equation: _____

STEP 3 Represent two negative integers.

$$(-6) + (-4)$$

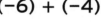

Find the sum.

STEP 4

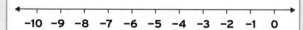

Equation: _____

2

STEP 1 Represent two positive integers.

$$2 + 8$$

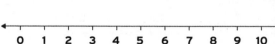

STEP 2 Find the sum.

Equation: _____

STEP 3 Represent two negative integers.

$$(-7) + (-2)$$

Find the sum.

STEP 4

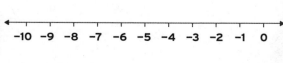

Equation: _____

BLOCK 9

addend *(n)* the number you combine with another number in an addition expression

> **PRACTICE**

3

$$3 + 5$$

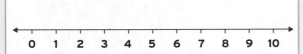

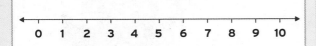

Equation: _____

4

$$7 + 2$$

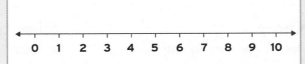

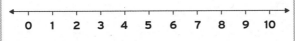

Equation: _____

5

$$(-8) + (-2)$$

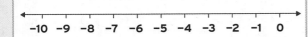

Equation: _____

6

$$(-4) + (-4)$$

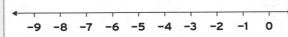

Equation: _____

> **Find the sum.**

$$(-6) + (-6)$$

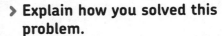

Equation: _____

> **Explain how you solved this problem.**

I solved this problem by _____

_____

_____

_____

_____

_____

TOPIC 3

TOPIC 2

TOPIC 1

SCORE ⓪ ① ②

Develop Strategies With Integers

I know that placing two numbers as far apart as I can will give me a higher score.

RULES

Number Jump! (Level 2)

What You Need
- *mSpace* pages 206–209
- number cube (green, 1–6)

What to Know
- Players roll for a new starting number each round.
- When finding the distance, ignore direction. The distance in this game is always positive.
- The score for each round is the distance between the two numbers.

How to Win
- After 7 rounds, players add their scores. The player with the highest score is the winner.

> HOW TO PLAY

STEP 1 Player A rolls the number cube to get a starting number. Player B decides on the sign.

ROUND	STARTING NUMBER
1	−2

STEP 2 Player A rolls the number cube, determines the sign, and jumps from the first to second number.

ROUND	STARTING NUMBER	NUMBER JUMPED TO
1	−2	4

STEP 3 Find the distance using the number line.

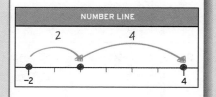

NUMBER LINE

STEP 4 Record the score. Trade turns.

SCORE (DISTANCE)

6

BLOCK 9

Number Jump! (Level 2)

> Record your numbers and use the number line to find the distance.
> Optional: Use the space on page 209 for calculations.

ROUND	STARTING NUMBER	NUMBER JUMPED TO	NUMBER LINE	SCORE (DISTANCE)
1			−12 −11 −10 −9 −8 −7 −6 −5 −4 −3 −2 −1 0 1 2 3 4 5 6 7 8 9 10 11 12	
2			−12 −11 −10 −9 −8 −7 −6 −5 −4 −3 −2 −1 0 1 2 3 4 5 6 7 8 9 10 11 12	
3			−12 −11 −10 −9 −8 −7 −6 −5 −4 −3 −2 −1 0 1 2 3 4 5 6 7 8 9 10 11 12	
4			−12 −11 −10 −9 −8 −7 −6 −5 −4 −3 −2 −1 0 1 2 3 4 5 6 7 8 9 10 11 12	
5			−12 −11 −10 −9 −8 −7 −6 −5 −4 −3 −2 −1 0 1 2 3 4 5 6 7 8 9 10 11 12	
6			−12 −11 −10 −9 −8 −7 −6 −5 −4 −3 −2 −1 0 1 2 3 4 5 6 7 8 9 10 11 12	
7			−12 −11 −10 −9 −8 −7 −6 −5 −4 −3 −2 −1 0 1 2 3 4 5 6 7 8 9 10 11 12	

MY TOTAL SCORE

RECORDING SHEET
Number Jump! (Level 2)

> Record your numbers and use the number line to find the distance.
Optional: Use the space on page 209 for calculations.

ROUND	STARTING NUMBER	NUMBER JUMPED TO	NUMBER LINE	SCORE (DISTANCE)
1			−12 −11 −10 −9 −8 −7 −6 −5 −4 −3 −2 −1 0 1 2 3 4 5 6 7 8 9 10 11 12	
2			−12 −11 −10 −9 −8 −7 −6 −5 −4 −3 −2 −1 0 1 2 3 4 5 6 7 8 9 10 11 12	
3			−12 −11 −10 −9 −8 −7 −6 −5 −4 −3 −2 −1 0 1 2 3 4 5 6 7 8 9 10 11 12	
4			−12 −11 −10 −9 −8 −7 −6 −5 −4 −3 −2 −1 0 1 2 3 4 5 6 7 8 9 10 11 12	
5			−12 −11 −10 −9 −8 −7 −6 −5 −4 −3 −2 −1 0 1 2 3 4 5 6 7 8 9 10 11 12	
6			−12 −11 −10 −9 −8 −7 −6 −5 −4 −3 −2 −1 0 1 2 3 4 5 6 7 8 9 10 11 12	
7			−12 −11 −10 −9 −8 −7 −6 −5 −4 −3 −2 −1 0 1 2 3 4 5 6 7 8 9 10 11 12	

MY TOTAL SCORE

> **Optional: Use this space for calculations.**

EXIT
Ticket

BLOCK
9

TOPIC 3

TOPIC 2

TOPIC 1

> **Answer this question.**

You are playing *Number Jump!* You marked −2 on your number line and then rolled a 6. Would you make the 6 positive or negative? Explain your answer.

I would make the 6 _____

because _____

_____

_____

_____

_____

SCORE ⓪ ① ②

CAREER EXPLORATION

> **Marine geologists explore the depths of the oceans.**

How might a marine geologist use integers to measure how deep oceans are?

> WORKED EXAMPLE

> TRY IT

> PRACTICE

STEP 1 Find the sign of the sum.

$$(-9) + 5$$

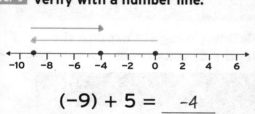

Sign of Sum: _negative_

STEP 2 Find the difference.

Difference: _9 − 5 = 4_

Equation: _(−9) + 5 = −4_

STEP 3 Verify with a number line.

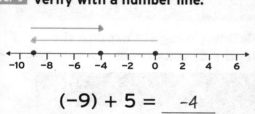

$$(-9) + 5 = \underline{\quad -4 \quad}$$

1

STEP 1 Find the sign of the sum.

$$(-9) + 7$$

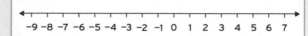

Sign of Sum: _____

STEP 2 Find the difference.

Difference: _____

Equation: _____

STEP 3 Verify with a number line.

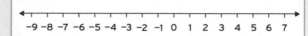

$$(-9) + 7 = \underline{\quad\quad}$$

2

STEP 1 Find the sign of the sum.

$$(-12) + 5$$

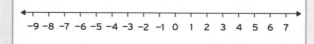

Sign of Sum: _____

STEP 2 Find the difference.

Difference: _____

Equation: _____

STEP 3 Verify with a number line.

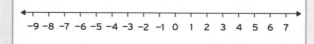

$$(-12) + 5 = \underline{\quad\quad}$$

additive inverse *(n)* the number you add to another number to get a sum of 0

3
$$29 + (-34)$$

Sign of Sum: _____

Difference: _____

Equation: _____

4
$$(-18) + 67$$

Sign of Sum: _____

Difference: _____

Equation: _____

5
$$72 + (-48)$$

Sign of Sum: _____

Difference: _____

Equation: _____

6
$$58 + (-45)$$

Sign of Sum: _____

Difference: _____

Equation: _____

7
$$(-98) + 89$$

Sign of Sum: _____

Difference: _____

Equation: _____

8
$$112 + (-127)$$

Sign of Sum: _____

Difference: _____

Equation: _____

EXIT Ticket

BLOCK **9**

> **Find the errors and fix them.**

Check these equations. If there is an error, rewrite the equation with the correct sum.

a. $(-3) + 5 = 8$

_____

b. $6 + (-10) = -4$

_____

c. $17 + (-13) = -4$

_____

d. $(-29) + 45 = 16$

_____

e. $58 + (-101) = -159$

_____

TOPIC 3

TOPIC 2

TOPIC 1

When I have a hard time adding positive and negative integers, I draw a number line to help me visualize the addition.

SCORE ⓪ ① ②

LESSON 4
CONCEPT

Add Numbers With Different Signs

> **WORKED EXAMPLE**

> **TRY IT**

> **PRACTICE**

WORKED EXAMPLE

STEP 1 Identify the sign of the sum.

$$(-4\frac{3}{4}) + 2\frac{5}{8}$$

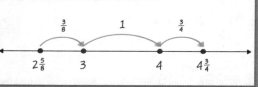

Sign of Sum: __negative__

STEP 2 Find the difference.

STEP 3 Add the jumps.

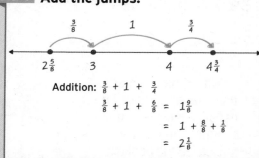

Addition: $\frac{3}{8} + 1 + \frac{3}{4}$

$$\frac{3}{8} + 1 + \frac{6}{8} = 1\frac{9}{8}$$
$$= 1 + \frac{8}{8} + \frac{1}{8}$$
$$= 2\frac{1}{8}$$

STEP 4 Write an equation.

Equation: $\underline{(-4\frac{3}{4}) + 2\frac{5}{8} = -2\frac{1}{8}}$

TRY IT

1

STEP 1 Identify the sign of the sum.

$$3.45 + (-6.2)$$

-7 -6 -5 -4 -3 -2 -1 0 1 2 3 4

Sign of sum: _____

STEP 2 Find the difference.

STEP 3 Add the jumps.

Addition:

STEP 4 Write an equation.

Equation: _____

PRACTICE

2

STEP 1 Identify the sign of the sum.

$$(-2\frac{5}{8}) + 5\frac{1}{2}$$

-3 -2 -1 0 1 2 3 4 5 6

Sign of sum: _____

STEP 2 Find the difference.

STEP 3 Add the jumps.

Addition:

STEP 4 Write an equation.

Equation: _____

open number line *(n)* A horizontal or vertical open-ended number line without tick marks or labels; the open number line can be used to record the distance or difference between two numbers.

> **PRACTICE**

3

$$(-4.75) + 7.5$$

-5 -4 -3 -2 -1 0 1 2 3 4 5 6 7 8

Sign of sum: _____

Addition:

Equation: _____

4

$$3\frac{1}{3} + \left(-7\frac{5}{6}\right)$$

-8 -7 -6 -5 -4 -3 -2 -1 0 1 2 3 4

Sign of sum: _____

Addition:

Equation: _____

> **Find the sum.**

$$2\frac{7}{10} + \left(-\frac{3}{5}\right)$$

TOPIC 3

-2 -1 0 1 2 3

Sign of sum: _____

TOPIC 2

Addition:

Equation: _____

TOPIC 1

> **How do you know whether the sum is positive or negative?**

I know the solution is _____

because _____

_____

_____

SCORE ⓪ ① ②

LESSON 5

Solve Problems With Positive and Negative Numbers

> WORKED EXAMPLE

> TRY IT

> PRACTICE

Worked Example

Read It! Read the problem.

MARINE GEOLOGIST

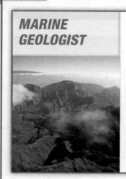

A mountain in Hawaii measures 13,800 ft above and 19,700 ft below sea level. Alex is 30,000 ft above the base. How far above sea level is Alex?

Show It! Represent the problem.

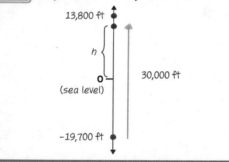

13,800 ft

h

0 (sea level)

30,000 ft

−19,700 ft

Solve It! Solve the problem.

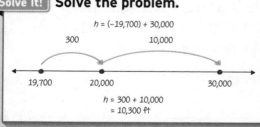

$h = (-19,700) + 30,000$

300   10,000

19,700   20,000   30,000

$h = 300 + 10,000$
$= 10,300$ ft

Check It! Check your work.

1 Try It

Read It! Read the problem.

NAVIGATOR

Mumbai

Lima   Equator

The equator has a latitude of 0°. The latitude of Lima, Peru, is −12°. The latitude of Mumbai, India, is 31° north of Lima. How far north of the equator is Mumbai?

Show It! Represent the problem.

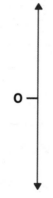

0

Solve It! Solve the problem.

Check It! Check your work.

2 Practice

Read It! Read the problem.

METEOROLOGIST

On January 23, 1971, the low temperature in Prospect Creek, Alaska, was −80°F. The temperature climbed 16° that day. What was the high temperature that day?

Show It! Represent the problem.

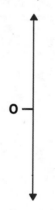

0

Solve It! Solve the problem.

Check It! Check your work.

When solving problems involving positive and negative numbers, drawing a vertical number line can help me understand the problem correctly.

3

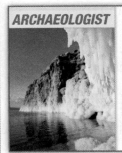

ARCHAEOLOGIST The Dead Sea is below sea level. The greatest depth of the Dead Sea is –2625 ft and its surface is 1237 ft above this depth. What is the depth at the Dead Sea's surface?

o –

4

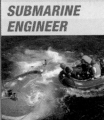

SUBMARINE ENGINEER The Mariana trench is the deepest place on Earth. A submarine reaches the trench at –6.8 mi below sea level and rises 3.3 mi. What is the depth of the submarine now?

o –

EXIT Ticket

BLOCK 9

> **Solve this problem.**

In January 1913 the coldest temperature at Death Valley in California was –10°C. By July 1913 the temperature had climbed by 67°C. What was the temperature in July?

o –

TOPIC 3

TOPIC 2

TOPIC 1

SCORE ⓪ ① ②

Number Strings

› Subtract this set of expressions mentally.

$139 - 60 =$ _____

$138 - 59 =$ _____

$114 - 90 =$ _____

$112 - 88 =$ _____

› Choose one expression and explain how you subtracted it mentally.

I subtracted _____ – _____

mentally by _____

_____

Make an Estimate

› Write whether the difference will be positive or negative without doing the actual subtraction.

$(-5) - 9$ _____ $6 - (-4)$ _____

$4 - (-7)$ _____ $(-4) - 6$ _____

$(-7) - (-11)$ _____ $12 - 9$ _____

$(-8) - (-3)$ _____ $9 - 12$ _____

› Choose an equation with a negative difference. How do you know the answer will be negative?

I know _____ – _____ will have

a negative difference because

_____

Missing Numbers

› Solve this puzzle by filling in the missing numbers.

3	–		=	4
–	■	+	■	–
	+		=	
=	■	=	■	=
8	–	2	=	

› How did you begin solving this puzzle?

I began solving this puzzle by

_____

_____

LESSON 4

Build It

> Build subtraction equations with a distance of 10. List possible equations using numbers from −20 to 0.

- _____
- _____
- _____
- _____
- _____
- _____
- _____
- _____

> **What strategy did you use to write the equations?**

The strategy I used to write the

equations was _____

_____

_____

LESSON 5

Brain Teaser

> **Solve this riddle.**

- I am an integer.

- If you add me to 3, the sum is negative.

- If you add me to 5, the sum is positive.

What integer am I? _____

> **How do you know your answer is correct?**

I know that _____ is correct

because _____

_____

_____

> **In this Topic, you learned to subtract positive and negative numbers.**

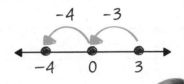

I use an open number line to subtract (−4) − 3.

$$(-4) - 3 = -7$$

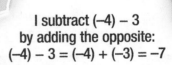

I subtract (−4) − 3 by adding the opposite:
$$(-4) - 3 = (-4) + (-3) = -7$$

LESSON 1
CONCEPT

Find Distance to Subtract

› WORKED EXAMPLE

› TRY IT

› PRACTICE

WORKED EXAMPLE

STEP 1 Plot positive integers on a number line.

$$4 - 7$$

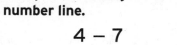

STEP 2 Find the distance.

STEP 3 Name the difference.

$$4 - 7$$

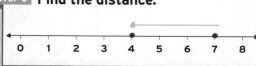

Direction of move: _negative_

Equation: _4 – 7 = –3_

STEP 4 Subtract two negative integers.

$$(-3) - (-8)$$

5

Direction of move: _positive_

Equation: _(–3) – (–8) = 5_

TRY IT

1

STEP 1 Plot the integers on a number line.

$$(-8) - (-2)$$

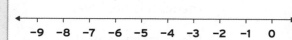

STEP 2 Find the distance.

STEP 3 Name the difference.

Direction of move: _____

Equation: _____

PRACTICE

2

STEP 1 Plot the integers on a number line.

$$3 - 8$$

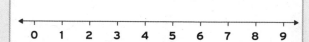

STEP 2 Find the distance.

STEP 3 Name the difference.

Direction of move: _____

Equation: _____

difference *(n)* The result of subtraction; the amount left over when an amount is subtracted from another amount.

3

$$4 - 10$$

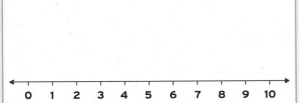

Direction of move: _____

Equation: _____

4

$$2 - 9$$

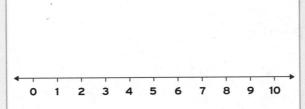

Direction of move: _____

Equation: _____

5

$$(-3) - (-5)$$

Direction of move: _____

Equation: _____

6

$$(-2) - (-7)$$

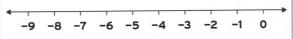

Direction of move: _____

Equation: _____

EXIT Ticket

BLOCK 9

> **Find the difference.**

$$(-3) - (-19)$$

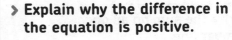

Direction of move: _____

Equation: _____

> **Explain why the difference in the equation is positive.**

The difference in the equation

is positive because _____

_____

_____

_____

TOPIC 3

TOPIC 2

TOPIC 1

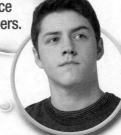

I can use a number line to subtract by finding the distance between two numbers.

SCORE ⓪ ① ②

LESSON 2
CONCEPT

Subtract Positive and Negative Integers

> **WORKED EXAMPLE**   > **TRY IT**   > **PRACTICE**

STEP 1 Rewrite the expression with addition.

$$7 - (-9)$$

Rewrite: ___7 + 9___

STEP 2 Solve the addition expression.

Rewrite: ___7 + 9 = 16___

STEP 3 Verify the sum on an open number line.

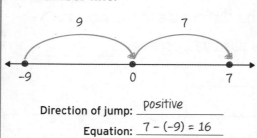

Direction of jump: ___positive___

Equation: ___7 − (−9) = 16___

1

STEP 1 Rewrite the expression with addition.

$$(-12) - 5$$

Rewrite: _____

STEP 2 Solve the addition expression.

STEP 3 Verify the sum on an open number line.

Direction of Jump: _____

Equation: _____

2

STEP 1 Rewrite the expression with addition.

$$(-9) - 4$$

Rewrite: _____

STEP 2 Solve the addition expression.

STEP 3 Verify the sum on an open number line.

Direction of Jump: _____

Equation: _____

opposite of a number *(n)* The number that, when added to another number, gives a sum of zero.

> PRACTICE

3

$(-8) - 3$

Rewrite: _____

<----------------------->

Equation: _____

4

$(-10) - 2$

Rewrite: _____

<----------------------->

Equation: _____

5

$8 - (-9)$

Rewrite: _____

<----------------------->

Equation: _____

6

$9 - (-13)$

Rewrite: _____

<----------------------->

Equation: _____

BLOCK
9

> **Find the errors and fix them.**

TOPIC 3

$(-4) - 5 = 9$

$6 - (-10) = -16$

$(-9) - 11 = -2$

TOPIC 2

Changing a subtraction expression to add the opposite works with all types of numbers:

$10 - 5 = 5$
has the same
solution as $10 + (-5) = 5$.

TOPIC 1

SCORE ⓪ ① ②

Subtracting Rational Numbers **221**

Subtract Positive and Negative Numbers

> WORKED EXAMPLE

> TRY IT

> PRACTICE

STEP 1 **Rewrite the expression with addition.**

$$(-4\tfrac{5}{8}) - 1\tfrac{3}{4}$$

Rewrite: $(-4\tfrac{5}{8}) + (-1\tfrac{3}{4})$

STEP 2 **Solve the addition expression.**

Rewrite: $(-4\tfrac{5}{8}) + (-1\tfrac{3}{4})$

Addition: $4\tfrac{5}{8} + 1\tfrac{3}{4}$

$4\tfrac{5}{8} + 1\tfrac{6}{8} = 5\tfrac{11}{8}$

$= 5 + \tfrac{8}{8} + \tfrac{3}{8}$

$= 6\tfrac{3}{8}$

STEP 3 **Verify the sum on an open number line.**

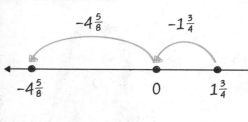

$-4\tfrac{5}{8}$ $-1\tfrac{3}{4}$

$-4\tfrac{5}{8}$ 0 $1\tfrac{3}{4}$

Equation: $(-4\tfrac{5}{8}) - 1\tfrac{3}{4} = -6\tfrac{3}{8}$

1

STEP 1 **Rewrite the expression with addition.**

$$(-3.7) - 2.5$$

Rewrite: _____

STEP 2 **Solve the addition expression.**

Addition:

STEP 3 **Verify the sum on an open number line.**

Equation: _____

2

STEP 1 **Rewrite the expression with addition.**

$$(-2\tfrac{1}{3}) - 4$$

Rewrite: _____

STEP 2 **Solve the addition expression.**

Addition:

STEP 3 **Verify the sum on an open number line.**

Equation: _____

3

$$(-5.5) - 1.25$$

Rewrite: _____

Addition:

Equation: _____

4

$$(-3\tfrac{1}{2}) - 5\tfrac{3}{4}$$

Rewrite: _____

Addition:

Equation: _____

EXIT Ticket

 BLOCK **9**

> **Find the difference.**

$$(-2\tfrac{4}{5}) - 1\tfrac{9}{10}$$

TOPIC 3

Rewrite: _____

Addition:

TOPIC 2

Equation: _____

> **Is it easier for you to find the difference using the open number line or by adding the opposite? Explain why.**

It is easier for me to find the

difference _____

because _____

_____

_____

TOPIC 1

SCORE ⓪ ① ②

LESSON 4
GAME

Use Distance Strategies With Integers

I don't need to draw an open number line. I can rewrite the expression by adding the opposite.

RULES

Number Jump! (Level 3)

What You Need
- *mSpace* pages 224–227
- number cube (green, 1–6)

How to Play
- Players decide who is A and B.
- Players decide if their numbers are positive or negative before sharing them with the other player.

How to Win
- After 7 rounds, the player with the most points is the winner.

> HOW TO PLAY

STEP 1 Both players roll the number cube. Decide whether each number is positive or negative.

Player A   Player B

GAME 1	PLAYER A	PLAYER B
ROUND	NUMBER	NUMBER
1	−4	+5

STEP 2 Record the subtraction expression: Player A's number minus Player B's number.

PLAYER A	PLAYER B	
NUMBER	NUMBER	SUBTRACTION PROBLEM
−4	+5	(−4) − 5

STEP 3 Use the number line to subtract and check.

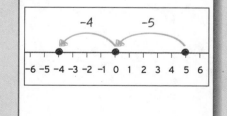

STEP 4 Record the difference. If the difference is negative, Player A scores a point. If it is positive, Player B scores a point.

	PLAYER A	PLAYER B
DIFFERENCE	POINTS	POINTS
−9	1	

BLOCK 9

Number Jump! (Level 3)

> Record the numbers rolled by you and your partner and record the subtraction expression.

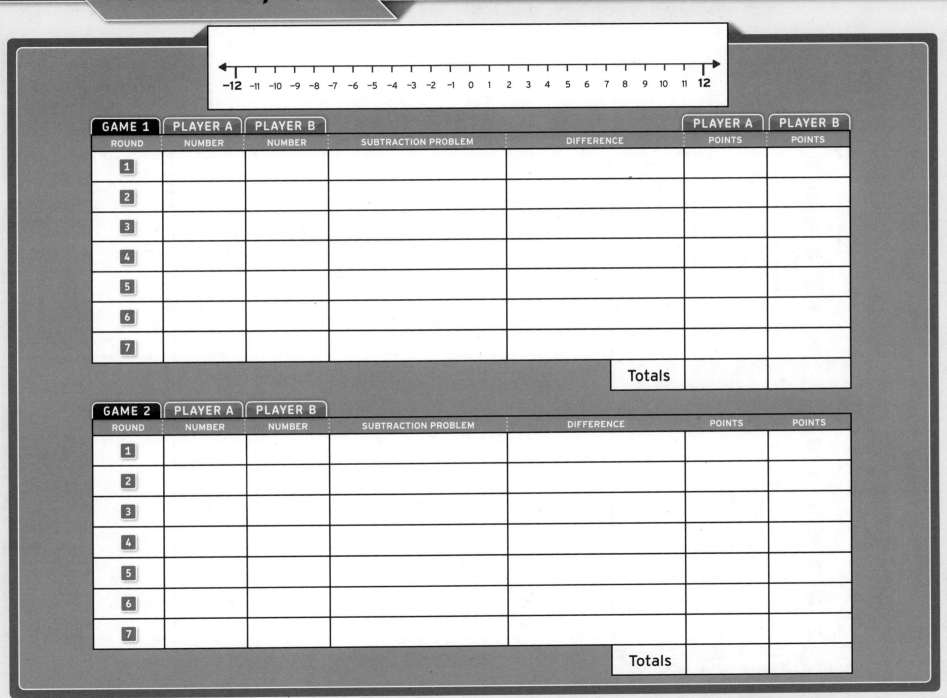

GAME 1	PLAYER A	PLAYER B			PLAYER A	PLAYER B
ROUND	NUMBER	NUMBER	SUBTRACTION PROBLEM	DIFFERENCE	POINTS	POINTS
1						
2						
3						
4						
5						
6						
7						
				Totals		

GAME 2	PLAYER A	PLAYER B				
ROUND	NUMBER	NUMBER	SUBTRACTION PROBLEM	DIFFERENCE	POINTS	POINTS
1						
2						
3						
4						
5						
6						
7						
				Totals		

RECORDING SHEET

Number Jump! (Level 3)

> Record the numbers rolled by you and your partner and record the subtraction expression.

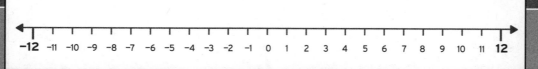

GAME 3	PLAYER A	PLAYER B			PLAYER A	PLAYER B
ROUND	NUMBER	NUMBER	SUBTRACTION PROBLEM	DIFFERENCE	POINTS	POINTS
1						
2						
3						
4						
5						
6						
7						
				Totals		

GAME 4	PLAYER A	PLAYER B				
ROUND	NUMBER	NUMBER	SUBTRACTION PROBLEM	DIFFERENCE	POINTS	POINTS
1						
2						
3						
4						
5						
6						
7						
				Totals		

> **Optional: Use this space for calculations.**

> **Answer this question.**

Player A rolls a 4 and Player B rolls a 6. Is it possible for Player A to score a point in this round? Explain.

It is/is not possible for Player A

to score a point in this round

because _____

_____

_____

_____

SCORE ⓪ ① ②

TOPIC 2

CAREER EXPLORATION

> **Oceanographers study the ocean to understand marine life better.**

Why would an oceanographer need to subtract integers when studying deep-sea creatures?

TOPIC 1

> WORKED EXAMPLE

> TRY IT

> PRACTICE

STEP 1 Analyze the problem.

Find *n*.

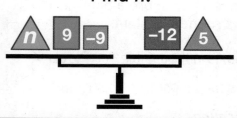

STEP 2 Write an equation for the problem.

$$n + 9 + (-9) = (-12) + 5$$

STEP 3 Solve the problem.

$$n = (-12) + 5$$
$$= -7$$

STEP 4 Check your work.

1

STEP 1 Analyze the problem.

Find *p*.

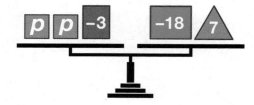

STEP 2 Write an equation for the problem.

STEP 3 Solve the problem.

STEP 4 Check your work.

2

STEP 1 Analyze the problem.

Find *x*.

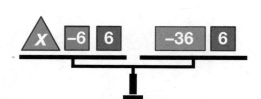

STEP 2 Write an equation for the problem.

STEP 3 Solve the problem.

STEP 4 Check your work.

3

Analyze the problem.

Find *n*.

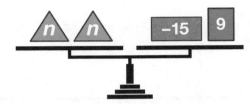

4

Analyze the problem.

Find *k*.

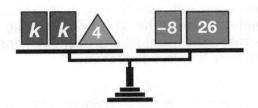

BLOCK

9

> Solve this problem.

Find *x*.

TOPIC 3

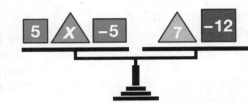

TOPIC 2

I check my answer with the equation I first wrote for this pan balance problem.

TOPIC 1

SCORE ⓪ ① ②

PERFORMANCE TASK

> **YOUR JOB**
> Meteorologist

> **YOUR TASK**
> Construct and interpret a scatter plot to investigate patterns in temperature and air quality.

ANCHOR VIDEO CONNECTION

As the Anchor Video shows, scientists gather and analyze data to explain events in nature.

Analyze Weather and Pollution Data

> In a town near a power plant, air quality is often very poor. One expert thinks that levels of pollutants increase when the air becomes warmer. Analyze data to evaluate this idea, and then research ways to improve air quality.

A EXPLORE

The table shows data gathered over 12 days in February. Fill in the empty column of the table by calculating the difference between the midnight and noon temperatures. The first difference is calculated for you.

Temperatures and Air Quality					
Date	Temperature at 12 A.M. (°C)	Temperature at 12 P.M. (°C)	Difference in Temperature (°C)	Pollutants (ppb)	Air Quality
1	−15	3	3 − (−15) = 18	32	Poor
2	−11	−5		10	Good
3	−15	8		52	Very Poor
4	−3	13		40	Very Poor
5	2	21		40	Very Poor
6	7	22		37	Poor
7	−5	21		45	Very Poor
8	−9	5		31	Poor
9	1	10		19	Good
10	15	18		5	Good
11	−7	17		49	Very Poor
12	−12	3		33	Poor

A **scatter plot** is a graph that shows the relationship between two sets of data. Make a scatter plot to compare the data sets from Part A. The point (18, 32) for Feb. 1 is plotted for you. It shows a difference in temperature of 18°C and a pollutant level of 32 parts per billion (ppb).

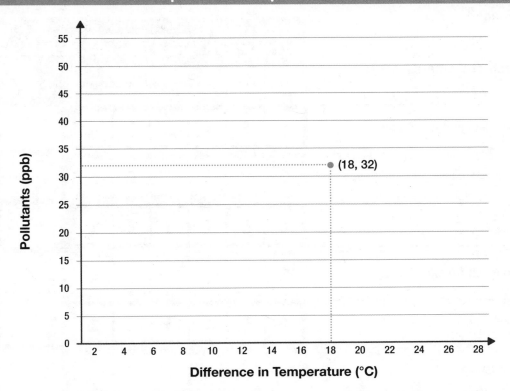

Difference in Temperature Compared to Levels of Pollutants

Pollutants (ppb)

Difference in Temperature (°C)

Evaluate

> **Rate how well you and your partner understood and completed each part of the performance task:**

Rating Guide			
None	Limited	Partial	Thorough
0	1	2	3

A Completed the data table and looked for patterns in the data.

Me	0	1	2	3
Partner	0	1	2	3

B Made a scatter plot of the data.

Me	0	1	2	3
Partner	0	1	2	3

C Answered the questions accurately.

Me	0	1	2	3
Partner	0	1	2	3

EXTEND

Research ways that air pollution from power plants can be reduced. Share your findings in an oral report or with presentation software.

C ANALYZE

INTERPRET What pattern in the data does the scatter plot show?

_____

_____

_____

PREDICT If the pattern in the data continues, when can the town expect the worst air pollution?

_____

_____

_____

Revisit the Mindset Scan

Congratulations, you've completed the final block of *MATH 180*.
Do you remember the Mindset Scan you took on the first day
of class? Take it again now to see if your mindset has changed.

> **Decide how much you agree or disagree with each statement.
> Circle and write your answer.**

		RATING SCALE						
		Choose a number on the left to agree or on the right to disagree.						
		Agree a lot	Agree	Agree a little	Disagree a little	Disagree	Disagree a lot	PROFILE NUMBER
A	No matter how much intelligence you have, you can always change it a good deal.	6	5	4	3	2	1	
B	You can learn new things, but you cannot really change your basic level of intelligence.	1	2	3	4	5	6	
C	I like my work best when it makes me think hard.	6	5	4	3	2	1	
D	I like my work best when I can do it really well without too much trouble.	1	2	3	4	5	6	
E	I like work that I'll learn from even if I make a lot of mistakes.	6	5	4	3	2	1	
F	I like my work best when I can do it perfectly without any mistakes.	1	2	3	4	5	6	
G	When something is hard, it just makes me want to work more on it, not less.	6	5	4	3	2	1	
H	To tell the truth, when I work hard, it makes me feel as though I'm not very smart.	1	2	3	4	5	6	

> **Add up all the profile numbers and write the total.**

TOTAL

Determine Your Mindset

> **If your profile number falls into this range:**

 **8–16**
You strongly believe that your intelligence is fixed—it doesn't change much. If you can't perform perfectly you would rather not do something. You think smart people don't have to work hard.

 **17–24**
You think that your intelligence doesn't change much. You prefer not to make mistakes if you can help it, and you also don't really like to put in a lot of work. You think learning should be easy.

 **25–32**
You are unsure about whether you can change your intelligence. You care about your performance and you also want to learn, but you don't really want to have to work too hard for it.

 **33–40**
You believe that you can increase your intelligence. You care about learning and you're willing to work hard. You want to do well, but you think it's more important to learn than to always perform well.

 **41–48**
You really feel sure that you can increase your intelligence by learning and you like a challenge. You believe that the best way to learn is to work hard, and you don't mind making mistakes while you do it.

After a few good teachers and a lot of perseverance, I ended up loving math and even choosing it as a major when I got to college.

Danica McKellar
Actress, and author of math books

Reflection Questions

Ⓐ Do you think your mindset has changed this year?

I think my mindset has (changed/not changed) because _____

_____

_____

_____

Ⓑ Why does a Growth Mindset help you learn?

A Growth Mindset helps me learn because _____

_____

_____

_____

Table of Contents

Multiplication Facts

> Use this table to help you remember multiplication facts.

✗	0	1	2	3	4	5	6	7	8	9	10	11	12
0	0	0	0	0	0	0	0	0	0	0	0	0	0
1	0	1	2	3	4	5	6	7	8	9	10	11	12
2	0	2	4	6	8	10	12	14	16	18	20	22	24
3	0	3	6	9	12	15	18	21	24	27	30	33	36
4	0	4	8	12	16	20	24	28	32	36	40	44	48
5	0	5	10	15	20	25	30	35	40	45	50	55	60
6	0	6	12	18	24	30	36	42	48	54	60	66	72
7	0	7	14	21	28	35	42	49	56	63	70	77	84
8	0	8	16	24	32	40	48	56	64	72	80	88	96
9	0	9	18	27	36	45	54	63	72	81	90	99	108
10	0	10	20	30	40	50	60	70	80	90	100	110	120
11	0	11	22	33	44	55	66	77	88	99	110	121	132
12	0	12	24	36	48	60	72	84	96	108	120	132	144

Symbols

› **Mathematicians use symbols to show relationships between numbers.**

SYMBOL	EXAMPLE	MEANING
$+$	$56.01 + 0.6$	plus or add
$-$	$\frac{3}{4} - \frac{1}{4}$	minus or subtract
$\times$	180×4	times or multiply
$\div$	$14 \div 7$	divide
$\overline{)}$	$7\overline{)14}$	divide
$-$	$\frac{14}{7}$	divide
$=$	$0.5 = \frac{1}{2}$	is equal to; shows equivalence
$\neq$	$\frac{1}{10} \neq 0.01$	is not equal to

SYMBOL	EXAMPLE	MEANING
$\approx$	$1.978 \approx 2$	is approximately equal to
$<$	$40 < 400$	is less than
$>$	$16 > 1.6$	is greater than
$\cdots$	$0.333333\ldots$	continues without end
$+$	$+4$	positive
$-$	-5	negative
$(\ )$	operations: $(3 + 4) - 2$ numbers: $5 - (-2)$	parentheses; shows what to evaluate first
$\{\ \}$	$\{0, 1, 2, 3, 4\}$	braces; shows members of a set
n	$14 + n = 34$	variable; represents an unknown quantity

> Knowing how measurements relate to one another helps you solve problems.

CONVERSIONS

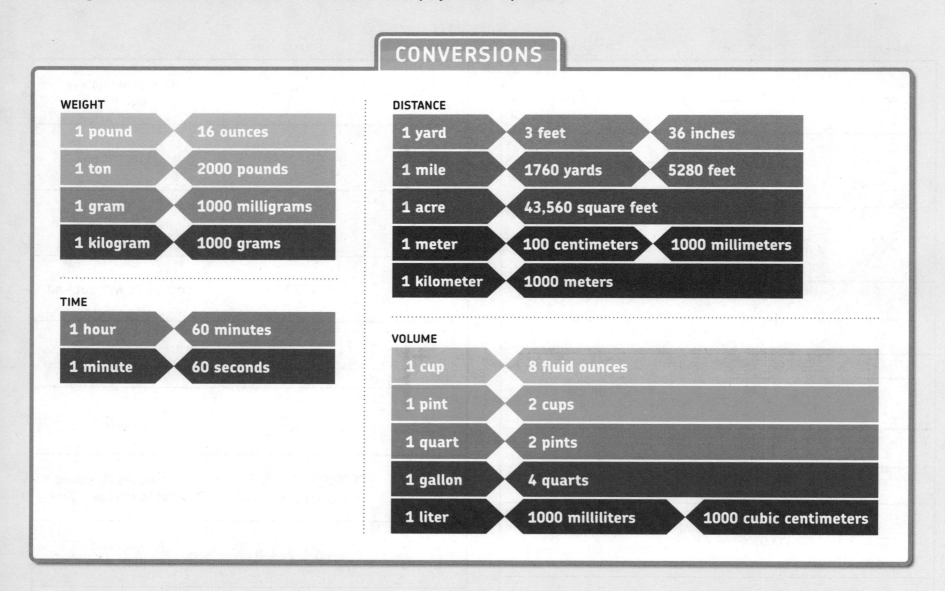

WEIGHT

1 pound	16 ounces
1 ton	2000 pounds
1 gram	1000 milligrams
1 kilogram	1000 grams

TIME

| 1 hour | 60 minutes |
| 1 minute | 60 seconds |

DISTANCE

1 yard	3 feet	36 inches
1 mile	1760 yards	5280 feet
1 acre	43,560 square feet	
1 meter	100 centimeters	1000 millimeters
1 kilometer	1000 meters	

VOLUME

1 cup	8 fluid ounces	
1 pint	2 cups	
1 quart	2 pints	
1 gallon	4 quarts	
1 liter	1000 milliliters	1000 cubic centimeters

perimeter	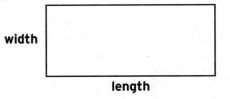	Perimeter of a rectangle = (2 × length) + (2 × width) $$P = 2l + 2w$$
area		Area of a rectangle = length × width $$A = l \times w$$
volume	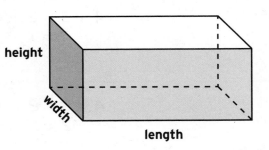	Volume of a rectangular prism = length × width × height $$V = l \times w \times h$$ Volume of a rectangular prism = Area of the base × height $$V = A \times h$$

> In mathematics, a property is a characteristic of a number or operation.

THE ASSOCIATIVE PROPERTY

PROPERTY	MEANING	EXAMPLE
Associative Property of Addition	The way we group three or more addends doesn't change the sum.	$(3 + 4) + 5 = 3 + (4 + 5)$ $7 + 5 = 3 + 9$ $12 = 12$
Associative Property of Multiplication	The way we group three or more factors doesn't change the product.	$(2 \times 3) \times 4 = 2 \times (3 \times 4)$ $6 \times 4 = 2 \times 12$ $24 = 24$

THE COMMUTATIVE PROPERTY

PROPERTY	MEANING	EXAMPLE
Commutative Property of Addition	Changing the order of the addends does not change the sum.	$4 + 3 = 3 + 4$ $7 = 7$
Commutative Property of Multiplication	Changing the order of the factors does not change the product.	$4 \times 3 = 3 \times 4$ $12 = 12$

THE DISTRIBUTIVE PROPERTY

PROPERTY	MEANING	EXAMPLE
Distributive Property of Multiplication	Multiplying a sum by a number is the same as adding the partial products.	$8 \times 24 = 8 \times (20 + 4)$ $= (8 \times 20) + (8 \times 4)$ $= 160 + 32$ $= 192$

THE IDENTITY PROPERTY

PROPERTY	MEANING	EXAMPLE
Additive Identity Property	Adding 0 to a number does not change the number's value.	$4 + 0 = 4$ or $0 + 4 = 4$
Multiplicative Identity Property	Multiplying a number by 1 does not change the number's value.	$7 \times 1 = 7$ or $1 \times 7 = 7$

THE INVERSE PROPERTY

PROPERTY	MEANING	EXAMPLE
Inverse Property of Addition	Adding a number to its opposite results in a sum of 0.	$5 + (-5) = 0$ or $(-5) + 5 = 0$
Inverse Property of Multiplication	Multiplying a number (excluding 0) by its reciprocal results in a product of 1.	$4 \times \frac{1}{4} = 1$ or $(-\frac{1}{4}) \times (-4) = 1$

Visual Models

> Visual models are helpful tools for representing and solving problems.

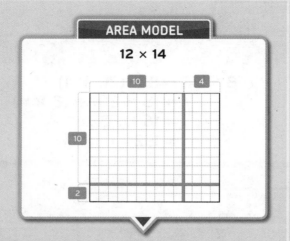

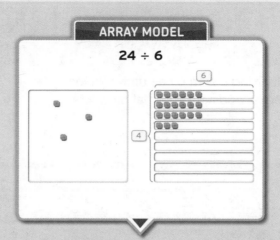

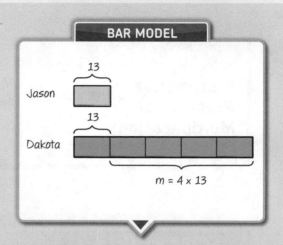

WHAT IS IT? An **Area Model** is a rectangle made up of equal-sized squares that can be used to find the product of two numbers.	An **Array Model** is used to arrange equal-sized objects in rows to represent equal groups in multiplication and division.	A **Bar Model** is made up of one or more rectangular bars that represent known and unknown quantities and their relationships.

WHY USE IT?

Use an Area Model to...
- multiply two factors
- find partial products when you use the Distributive Property to multiply
- use the Commutative Property to multiply

Use an Array Model to...
- represent multiplication
- identify factors of a number
- represent division
- represent parts of sets as fractions

Use a Bar Model to represent and solve...
- part-part-whole problems
- compare problems
- change problems
- equal groups problems

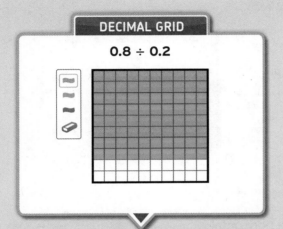

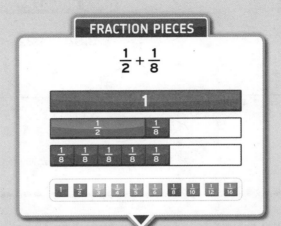

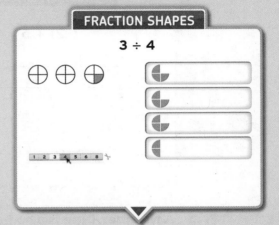

WHAT IS IT? A **Decimal Grid**, which represents one whole, is a 10 by 10 square that is divided into 100 squares. It is used to represent decimals.

Fraction Pieces are models that represent unit fractions and can be combined to form greater fractions.

Fraction Shapes are circular fraction models that are used to represent sharing situations.

WHY USE IT? Use a **Decimal Grid** to...
- represent decimals
- name fractions with denominators of 10 and 100 as decimals
- compare fractions and decimals
- apply place value to decimals

Use **Fraction Pieces** to...
- represent fractions
- compose fractions and wholes with unit fractions
- compare and order fractions
- solve problems with equivalent fractions
- add and subtract fractions

Use **Fraction Shapes** to...
- represent fractions as division
- represent fractions in multiplication and division problems

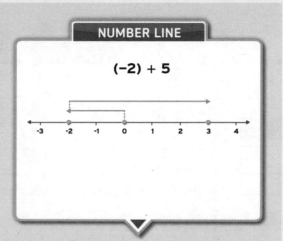

NUMBER LINE

(−2) + 5

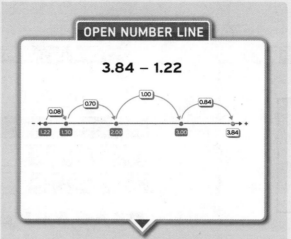

OPEN NUMBER LINE

3.84 − 1.22

WHAT IS IT?

A **Number Line** is a horizontal or vertical line labeled with tick marks at equal intervals. It is used to show relationships among numbers.

An **Open Number Line** is a horizontal or vertical line without tick marks that represents number relationships.

WHY USE IT?

Use a **Number Line** to...

- locate any number, including whole numbers, fractions, decimals, integers, and rational numbers
- add numbers
- subtract to find the distance between numbers
- compare and order numbers
- name decimals between decimals

Use an **Open Number Line** to...

- plot any number, including whole numbers, fractions, decimals, integers, and rational numbers
- add numbers
- subtract to find the distance between numbers

Problem-Solving Routine

> Use this routine to help you analyze and solve word problems.

STEPS	WHAT TO DO	EXAMPLE
Read It! **Read and identify the problem.**	▪ Read and understand the problem. ▪ Figure out what the problem is asking you to do. ▪ Identify the problem type. Is it a part-part-whole, change, compare, or equal groups problem?	**APP DESIGNER** Jason created 13 cell phone apps. Dakota created 5 times as many. How many more cell phone apps did Dakota create? PROBLEM TYPE _Compare Problem_
Show It! **Represent the problem.**	▪ Use a visual model to represent the problem. ▪ Remember to label all the quantities.	13 Jason ▭ 13 Dakota ▭▭▭▭▭ $m = 4 \times 13$
Solve It! **Solve the problem.**	▪ Write equations to represent the solution. ▪ Solve the problem.	4×13 $\wedge$ $10 + 3$ $4 \times 13 = (4 \times 10) + (4 \times 3)$ $\quad = \quad 40 \; + \; 12$ $m = 52$
Check It! **Check your work.**	▪ Check the steps and your work for reasonableness. ▪ You may want to estimate the solution or work backwards. ▪ Ask yourself, "Does my answer make sense?"	Estimate: $4 \times 10 = 40$ My answer is reasonable because __52__ is close to __40__ .

> Remember the four problem types when using the Bar Model.

PROBLEM TYPE	HOW TO TELL	EXAMPLE
Equal Groups Problems	▪ Look for multiple groups of equal size. ▪ The unknown in the problem can be the group size, the number of groups, or the total number in each group.	Mia designed a bookshelf with 6 shelves. Each shelf weighs 12 pounds. The frame weighs 38 pounds. What does the bookshelf weigh? *equal groups* 6×12 38 $t = (6 \times 12) + 38$
Compare Problems	▪ Look for unequal quantities that are being compared. ▪ The unknown in the problem can be one of the unequal quantities or the difference between them.	Jason created 13 cell phone apps. *first quantity* Dakota created 5 times as many. *second quantity* How many more cell phone apps did Dakota create? 13 Jason 13 Dakota $m = 4 \times 13$

PROBLEM TYPE	HOW TO TELL	EXAMPLE
Part-Part-Whole Problems	▪ Look for two or more quantities (parts) combined to make a total (whole). ▪ The unknown in the problem can be the parts or the whole.	Luis completed $\frac{1}{4}$ of his lab tests on Monday and $\frac{1}{3}$ of the tests on Tuesday. What fraction of the tests does he need to finish?
Change Problems	▪ Look for a starting quantity, a change in that quantity, and an ending quantity. ▪ The unknown (quantity to find) may be the starting quantity, the ending quantity, or the changed quantity.	Sunita has 42 comic books. She has 6 times as many comic books as Ben. Then, she gives half her comic books to Ben. How many comic books does Ben have now?

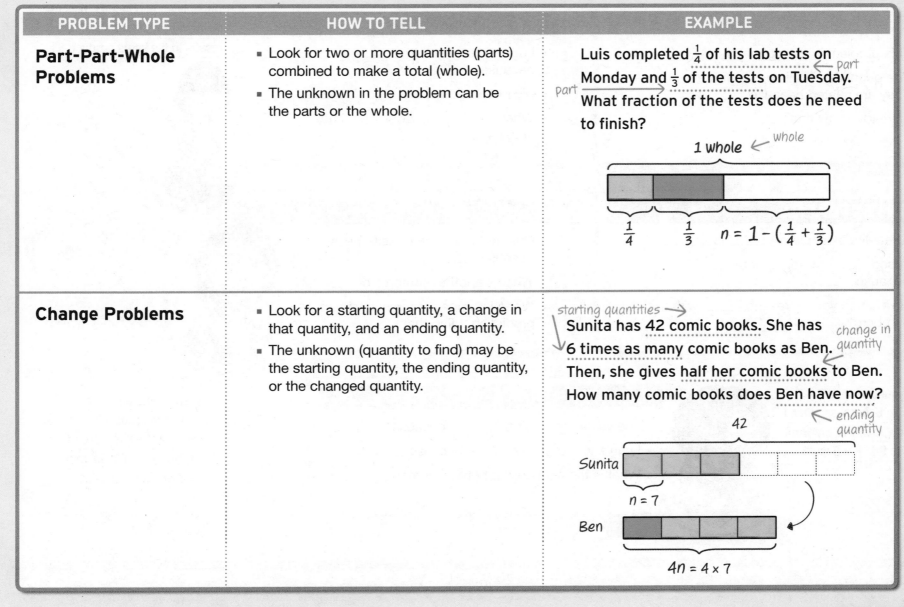

Talking About Math

> Use clear mathematical language to talk about math problems and concepts.

ANALYZE

- This problem is asking me to _____.
- The quantities in this problem are _____. They are related because _____.
- I already know that _____.

REASON

- I agree/disagree with _____ that _____ because _____.
- My idea builds upon _____'s because _____.
- When is _____ always/sometimes/ never true?

I agree with Juan that order doesn't matter when multiplying two factors because multiplying 9 × 7 and 7 × 9 results in the same product: 63.

CONTEXTUALIZE

- A real-life example of _____ is _____.
- I used _____ to represent _____ because _____.
- How could you represent _____ with numbers?

EVALUATE

- One tool I can use to help me is _____ because _____.
- What is another strategy for _____?
- When I compare my result with my prediction, I find that _____.

The quotient of 400 ÷ 5 can't be 8 because when I multiply to check my work, I see that 8 × 5 is 40.

IDENTIFY

- The value can/can't be _____ because _____ .
- I can find _____ by _____ because _____.
- What is the relationship between/among _____?

When I compare my result with my prediction, I find that my estimate 8 is close to my answer 7.03. So, my answer is reasonable.

I figured out what the problem is asking me to do by *drawing a bar model that shows that Jason created 13 apps and Dakota created 5 times as many*.

INFER

- I tried _____ and found out _____. Then I tried _____.
- I figured out what the problem is asking me to do by _____.
- What's another way to _____?

JUSTIFY

- I used the strategy of _____ because _____.
- Another example of _____ is _____.
- Does _____ still work if you _____?

I can represent the problem by *shading alternate colors on a decimal grid* because *I can show there are 4 groups of 0.2 in 0.8*.

REPRESENT

- I can represent the problem by _____ because _____.
- I can conclude that _____ because I know _____.
- The result makes sense because _____.

DEFINE

- I know the value _____ is appropriate for this situation because _____.
- The term/symbol _____ means _____.
- Can you explain how to _____?

GENERALIZE

- If _____, then the result will be _____ because _____.
- I notice that _____ will/won't always work because _____.
- _____ is a reasonable answer because _____.

If *you multiply two unit fractions*, then the product will be *less than both fractions* because *the denominator will be greater, resulting in a smaller fraction*.

A

MATH TERM	MEANING	EXAMPLE
add (verb)	To combine two or more numbers to find their *sum*. (see *addition*, *add to*)	$4 + 8 = 12$
add to (verb)	To increase a number by another number. (see *add*)	$37 + 4 = 41$
addend (noun)	The number you combine with another number in an addition *expression*. (see *addition*)	$\textcircled{4} + \textcircled{8} = 12$ addends
addition (noun)	The *operation* of combining two or more numbers. (see *add*)	$4 + 8 = 12$
Additive Identity Property (noun)	Adding *zero* to a number does not change the number's *value*. (see *add*, *property*)	$4 + 0 = 4$ or $0 + 4 = 4$
additive inverse (noun)	The number you *add* to another number to get a *sum* of *zero*. (see *inverse operation*, *opposite of a number*)	$-4 + \textcircled{4} = 0$ additive inverse of -4
algebra (noun)	A branch of math that uses symbols, usually letters, to represent *unknown* numbers. (see *symbol*, *variable*)	$3 + a = 4$ $a = 1$
algebraic expression (noun)	An *expression* that uses variables to represent *unknown* quantities. (see *quantity*, *variable*)	$8p$ $x + 3$ $2(a - b)$

MATH TERM	MEANING	EXAMPLE
area (noun)	The measure of the amount of space inside a flat figure; area is measured in square units; the *formula* for the area of a rectangle is $A = l \times w$, where *l* and *w* represent the length and the width. (see *volume*)	$A = 5 \times 7$ The area of the rectangle is 35 square units. 7 5
array (noun)	An arrangement of objects or numbers in rows and columns; can be used to represent *multiplication* or *division*.	$6 \times 4 = 24$ $4 \times 3 = 12$ $24 \div 6 = 4$ $12 \div 4 = 3$ 6 4
Associative Property of Addition (noun)	The way we group three or more addends doesn't change the *sum*. (see *addend*, *property*)	$(3 + 4) + 5 = 3 + (4 + 5)$ $7 + 5 = 3 + 9$ $12 = 12$
Associative Property of Multiplication (noun)	The way we group three or more factors doesn't change the *product*. (see *factor*, *property*)	$(2 \times 3) \times 4 = 2 \times (3 \times 4)$ $6 \times 4 = 2 \times 12$ $24 = 24$

B

MATH TERM	MEANING	EXAMPLE
benchmark numbers (noun)	Familiar numbers that you use to make comparisons and estimates. (see *estimate*, *one-half*, *zero*)	$\frac{1}{3}$ $\frac{1}{3}$ $\frac{1}{3}$ $\frac{1}{3}$ 1 $\frac{1}{6}$ $\frac{1}{6}$ $\frac{1}{6}$ $\frac{1}{6}$ $\frac{1}{6}$ $\frac{4}{3} > \textcircled{1}$ benchmark $\frac{5}{6} < \textcircled{1}$

C

MATH TERM	MEANING	EXAMPLE
common denominator (noun)	The *denominator* of two or more fractions that have the same denominator. (see *fraction*)	$\frac{5}{\textcircled{8}}$ $\frac{7}{\textcircled{8}}$ common denominator

MATH TERM	MEANING	EXAMPLE
common factor *(noun)*	A *factor* of two or more numbers that have the same factor. (see *factors of a number*, *greatest common factor*)	factors of 8: <u>1, 2, 4, 8</u> factors of 12: <u>1, 2, 3, 4, 6, 12</u> common factors of 8 and 12: <u>1, 2, 4</u>
common numerator *(noun)*	The *numerator* of two or more fractions that have the same numerator. (see *fraction*)	common numerator $\frac{3}{4}$ $\frac{3}{16}$
Commutative Property of Addition *(noun)*	Changing the order of the addends does not change the *sum*. (see *addend*, *property*)	$4 + 3 = 3 + 4$ $7 = 7$
Commutative Property of Multiplication *(noun)*	Changing the order of the factors does not change the *product*. (see *factor*, *property*)	$4 \times 3 = 3 \times 4$ $12 = 12$
decimal number *(noun)*	A number with digits arranged by *place value*; we usually refer to numbers as decimals only if there is a *decimal point* followed by digits. (see *digit*)	2654.387 decimal number
decimal point *(noun)*	A *symbol* (dot or period) used to separate the *whole number* part from the fractional part in a *decimal number*.	0.8 decimal point
denominator *(noun)*	Tells the total number of *equal* parts in the *whole* in a *fraction*; the number below the *fraction bar* in a fraction.	$\frac{3}{4}$ denominator

MATH TERM	MEANING	EXAMPLE
difference *(noun)*	The result of *subtraction*; the amount left over when an amount is subtracted from another amount.	$5 - 1 = 4$ difference
digit *(noun)*	One of the symbols 0, 1, 2, 3, 4, 5, 6, 7, 8, and 9 when written in a number; its *value* is determined by its place in a number. (see *symbol*, *place value*)	12,563 five-digit number
Distributive Property *(noun)*	Multiplying a *sum* by a number is the same as adding the *partial products*. (see *multiply*)	$8 \times 24 = 8 \times (20 + 4)$ $= (8 \times 20) + (8 \times 4)$ $= \quad 160 \quad + \quad 32$ $= \quad 192$
divide *(verb)*	To split into *equal* parts or groups. (see *division*, *equal groups*)	$6\overline{)24}$ $24 \div 6 = 4$ $\frac{24}{6} = 4$
dividend *(noun)*	The number that is divided into *equal* parts or groups; the number you *divide*. (see *equal groups*)	dividend $24 \div 6 = 4$ $6\overline{)24}$ $\frac{24}{6} = 4$ dividend dividend
divisible *(adjective)*	Able to *divide* a *dividend* with no *remainder*.	$12 \div 3 = 4$ $14 \div 3 = 4 \text{ R2}$ divisible by 3 not divisible by 3
division *(noun)*	The *operation* of creating *equal* parts from a number or creating *equal groups* in a set. (see *divide*)	$6\overline{)24}$ $24 \div 6 = 4$ $\frac{24}{6} = 4$

D

MATH TERM	MEANING	EXAMPLE
divisor (noun)	The number you *divide* by. (see *divide*)	$24 \div 6 = 4$ $6)\overline{24}$ with quotient 4 $\frac{24}{6} = 4$ divisor
E		
equal (adjective)	Having the same amount. (see *equation, equivalent, inequality*)	$11 + 7 = 18$ 60 seconds = 1 minute 1 dollar = 100 cents
equal groups (noun)	Collections that each have the same number of items. (see *divide, division, multiply, multiplication*)	3 equal groups of 6
equation (noun)	A mathematical sentence in which the values on both sides of the *equal* sign are the same (equal). (see *equivalent, evaluate, expression, value*)	$3 + 7 = 10$ $20 = 5 \times 4$
equivalent (adjective)	Having the same meaning or having the same amount. (see *equal, equation, equivalent fractions*)	5×4 is equivalent to 5 groups of 4 5×4 is equivalent to $10 + 10$ 5×4 is equivalent to 2×10
equivalent fractions (noun)	Two or more fractions that name the same part of a *whole*. (see *equal, equivalent*)	$\frac{3}{4} = \frac{6}{8}$
estimate (noun)	A number that is an approximate calculation based on numbers that are easier to work with; is close to the exact answer. (see *estimation*)	$10.12 + 9.22$ $10 + 9 = 19$ estimate

MATH TERM	MEANING	EXAMPLE
estimate (verb)	To approximate a calculation using numbers that are easier to work with. (see *estimation*)	$10.12 + 9.22$ $10 + 9 = 19$ estimate
estimation (noun)	The process of approximating a calculation by using numbers that are easier to work with; the result of estimation is close to the exact answer. (see *estimate*)	$10.12 + 9.22$ is close to $10 + 9$
evaluate (verb)	To find the *value* of. (see *equation, expression*)	If $x = 20$, then evaluate $100 \div x$ $100 \div 20 = 5$
even number (noun)	Any integer that is *divisible* by 2; not an *odd number*. (see *integers*)	even numbers: $\ldots -4, -2, 0, 2, 4, 6, 8, 10 \ldots$
expanded form (noun)	A number written as the *sum* of the values of each *digit* based on its *place value*. (see *value*)	$135 = 100 + 30 + 5$ $3.14 = 3 + 0.1 + 0.04$
expression (noun)	A grouping of numbers and/or variables and *operation* symbols; does not have an *equal* sign or is on one side of an equal sign. (see *equation, evaluate, symbol, variable*)	$2n + 4 = 4 \times 10$ expression

F

MATH TERM	MEANING	EXAMPLE
factor (noun)	The number you *multiply* to find a *product*. (see *factors of a number*)	$4 \times 5 = 20$ *factors*
factors of a number (noun)	The numbers that *divide* exactly, with no *remainder*, into a number. (see *factor, common factor, greatest common factor, multiple*)	$18 = 1 \times 18$ $18 = 2 \times 9$ $18 = 3 \times 6$ factors of 18: 1, 2, 3, 6, 9, 18
formula (noun)	A general rule that shows a relationship among variables in which the *value* of one *variable* is dependent on the value of other variables. (see *area, volume*)	8 3 Area = length × width
fraction (noun)	A number that names parts of a *whole* or parts of a set. (see *fraction bar, denominator, numerator*)	$\frac{1}{4}$ of a whole $\qquad$ $\frac{1}{4}$ of a set 1
fraction bar (noun)	The line that separates the *numerator* from the *denominator* of a *fraction*.	$\frac{3}{4}$ *fraction bar*
function table (noun)	A table that shows the relationship of one set of numbers to another set of numbers; one set is the input and the other is the output; the rule provides the way to determine an output for any input.	INPUT / EQUATIONS / OUTPUT 1 — 8 2 — 16 3 — 24 4 — 32 5 — $5 \times 8 = 40$ — 40 10 — $10 \times 8 = 80$ — 80 12 — $12 \times 8 = 96$ — 96 Output = Input × 8

G

MATH TERM	MEANING	EXAMPLE
greater than (adjective)	Has a *value* farther to the right on a *number line*; is a larger *quantity*; the *symbol* that expresses that one quantity is greater than another quantity is >, where the open side of the symbol faces the greater quantity. (see *less than*)	0 1 2 3 4 5 6 7 8 9 10 $10 > 8$ 10 is greater than 8
greatest common factor (noun)	The largest *common factor* of two or more numbers; the greatest common factor is also called the GCF. (see *factors of a number*)	factors of 8: 1, 2, 4, 8 factors of 12: 1, 2, 3, 4, 6, 12 *greatest common factor*

H

MATH TERM	MEANING	EXAMPLE
hundreds place (noun)	The third place to the left of the *decimal point*, which shows how many hundreds are in a number; the digit's *value* in that place is the *digit* times 100. (see *place value*)	2654.387 *hundreds place*
hundredths place (noun)	The second place to the right of the decimal point which shows how many hundredths are in a number; the digit's *value* in that place is the digit times $\frac{1}{100}$. (see *digit, place value*)	2654.387 *hundredths place*

I

MATH TERM	MEANING	EXAMPLE
inequality (noun)	A mathematical sentence that shows that two values are not *equal*. The symbols > (*greater than*), < (*less than*), ≠ (not equal to), and ≈ (approximately equal to) can be placed between the two numbers to show their relationships. (see *symbol, value*)	$1 + 4 < 6$ $910 > 901$ $14 + 36 \neq 40$ $0.97 \approx 1$

MATH TERM	MEANING	EXAMPLE
integers *(noun)*	Whole numbers, their opposites, and *zero*. (see *opposite of a number, positive number, negative number, whole number*)	... −5, −4, −3, −2, −1, 0, 1, 2, 3, 4, 5, ...
inverse operation *(noun)*	An *operation* that reverses the effect of another operation. (see *additive inverse, multiplicative inverse, Inverse Property of Addition, Inverse Property of Multiplication, opposite of a number*)	Addition and subtraction are inverse operations $3 + 4 = 7$ $7 − 4 = 3$ Multiplication and division are inverse operations $3 × 4 = 12$ $12 ÷ 4 = 3$
Inverse Property of Addition *(noun)*	Adding a number to its opposite results in a *sum* of zero. (see *add, inverse operation, opposite of a number, property*)	$5 + (−5) = 0$ and $(−5) + 5 = 0$
Inverse Property of Multiplication *(noun)*	Multiplying a number (excluding 0) by its reciprocal results in a *product* of 1. (see *inverse operation, multiplicative inverse, reciprocal of a number, property*)	$4 × \frac{1}{4} = 1$ or $(−\frac{1}{4}) × (−4) = 1$
L		
less than *(adjective)*	Has a *value* farther to the left on a *number line*; is a smaller *quantity*; the *symbol* that expresses that one quantity is less than another is <, where the small part of the symbol points to the smaller quantity. (see *greater than*)	 $8 < 10$ 8 is less than 10

MATH TERM	MEANING	EXAMPLE
M		
mixed number *(noun)*	A *fraction* greater than 1 that includes both a *whole number* part and a fractional part. (see *greater than*)	 mixed number $= 1\frac{57}{100}$
model *(noun)*	A mathematical *representation* of a mathematical or real-world situation; usually in the form of an *equation* or drawing.	 $t = (6 × 12) + 38$
multiple *(noun)*	A *product* of a given number and a *whole number*. (see *factors of a number, multiple of 10*)	multiple of 5: 5, 10, 15, 20, 25, ...
multiple of 10 *(noun)*	A number that has a *factor* of 10. (see *multiple*)	multiple of 10: 10, 20, 30, 40, 50, ...
multiplication *(noun)*	The *operation* of determining the total number of objects in *equal groups*. (see *multiply*)	$3 × 6 = 18$ 3 equal groups of 6 is 18
Multiplicative Identity Property *(noun)*	Multiplying a number by 1 does not change the number's *value*. (see *multiply, property*)	$4 × 1 = 4$ or $1 × 4 = 4$

MATH TERM	MEANING	EXAMPLE
multiplicative inverse (noun)	The number you *multiply* by another number to get a *product* of 1. (see *inverse operation*, *Inverse Property of Multiplication*, *reciprocal of a number*)	inverse of 6 inverse of $\frac{3}{4}$ $6 \times \frac{1}{6} = \frac{6}{6}$ $\frac{3}{4} \times \frac{4}{3} = \frac{12}{12}$ $= 1$ $= 1$
multiply (verb)	To determine the total number of objects in *equal groups*. (see *multiplication*)	5 groups of 2: $5 \times 2 = 10$ 3 groups of $\frac{1}{2}$: $3 \times \frac{1}{2} = \frac{3}{2}$
N		
negative (adjective)	On the left side of *zero* on a *number line*; the opposite of. (see *negative number*, *opposite of a number*, *positive*)	negative −9 −8 −7 −6 −5 −4 −3 −2 −1 0 1 2 3
negative number (noun)	Number to the left of *zero* on the *number line*; a number *less than* zero. (see *integers*, *negative*, *positive number*)	−9 −8 −7 −6 −5 −4 −3 −2 −1 0 1 2 3 negative numbers
number line (noun)	A line on which every point names one number and every number has a unique location.	−9 −8 −7 −6 −5 −4 −3 −2 −1 0 1 2 3
numerator (noun)	Tells how many *equal* parts of the *whole* a *fraction* is describing; the number above the *fraction bar* in a fraction.	numerator $\frac{3}{4}$

MATH TERM	MEANING	EXAMPLE
O		
odd number (noun)	Any integer that is not *divisible* by 2; not an *even number*. (see *integers*)	odd numbers: ... −5, −3, −1, 1, 3, 5, 7, ...
one-eighth (noun)	One part out of one *whole* that has been divided into eight *equal* parts; written as $\frac{1}{8}$. (see *divide, unit fraction*)	
one-fourth (noun)	One part out of one *whole* that has been divided into four *equal* parts; written as $\frac{1}{4}$. (see *unit fraction*)	
one-half (noun)	One part out of one *whole* that has been divided into two *equal* parts; written as $\frac{1}{2}$. (see *benchmark numbers*, *divide, unit fraction*)	
one-hundredth (noun)	One part out of one *whole* that has been divided into one hundred *equal* parts; written as $\frac{1}{100}$ or 0.01. (see *decimal number*, *hundredths place*, *unit fraction*)	one-hundredth
one-sixteenth (noun)	One part out of one *whole* that has been divided into sixteen *equal* parts; written as $\frac{1}{16}$. (see *divide, unit fraction*)	

MATH TERM	MEANING	EXAMPLE
one-sixth *(noun)*	One part out of one *whole* that has been divided into six *equal* parts; written as $\frac{1}{6}$. (see *divide, unit fraction*)	
one-tenth *(noun)*	One part out of one *whole* that has been divided into ten *equal* parts; written as $\frac{1}{10}$ or 0.1. (see *decimal number, divide, tenths place, unit fraction*)	one-tenth
one-third *(noun)*	One part out of one *whole* that has been divided into three *equal* parts; written as $\frac{1}{3}$. (see *divide, unit fraction*)	
one-twelfth *(noun)*	One part out of one *whole* that has been divided into twelve *equal* parts; written as $\frac{1}{12}$. (see *divide, unit fraction*)	
ones place *(noun)*	The first place to the left of the *decimal point*, which shows how many ones are in a number; the digit's *value* in that place is the *digit* times 1. (see *place value*)	2654.387 ones place
operation *(noun)*	A mathematical process; defined by a rule, performed on one or more numbers to get a resulting number; the most common operations are *addition, subtraction, multiplication,* and *division*.	$24 \div 6 = 4$ $10.12 + 9.22 = 19.34$ operation

MATH TERM	MEANING	EXAMPLE
opposite of a number *(noun)*	The number that when added to another number gives a *sum* of *zero*; on a *number line*, the number that is the same distance from 0 as another number but in the opposite direction from zero. (see *additive inverse, inverse operation, Inverse Property of Addition, negative*)	opposite of 4 $4 + (-4) = 0$ opposite of −4
order of operations *(noun)*	A rule that specifies which order to perform the operations in an *expression* with more than one *operation*: 1. parentheses 2. *multiply/divide* left to right 3. *add/subtract* left to right	$2 \times (5 - 2) + 3$ $2 \times 3 + 3$ $6 + 3 = 9$
P		
partial products *(noun)*	Numbers you *add* when you break one of the factors into a *sum* of its parts to calculate a *product*. (see *Distributive Property, factor*)	8×16 $8 \times (10 + 6)$ $(8 \times 10) + (8 \times 6)$ $80 + 48 = 128$ partial products
partial quotients *(noun)*	Numbers you *add* to calculate a *quotient*.	partial quotients 2 10 12 R3 $6 \overline{)75}$ -60 15 -12 3
pattern *(noun)*	An ordered set of numbers or objects arranged in a way that follows a rule.	53 34 9 21 18 4 6 102 1 pattern: multiples of 2

MATH TERM	MEANING	EXAMPLE
place value *(noun)*	The *value* of a *digit* in a number; for example, in 2654, 5 represents 5 tens or 50, because 5 is in the tens place. (see also *hundreds place, hundredths place, ones place, ten-thousandths place, tenths place, thousandths place, thousands place*)	2654 2 thousands or 2000 6 hundreds or 600 } place value 5 tens or 50 4 ones or 4
positive *(adjective)*	On the right side of zero on a *number line*.	positive −5 −4 −3 −2 −1 0 1 2 3 4 5
positive number *(noun)*	A number to the right of *zero* on the *number line*; a number *greater than* zero. (see *integers, positive, negative number*)	−5 −4 −3 −2 −1 0 1 2 3 4 5 positive numbers
prime number *(noun)*	A *whole number greater than* 1 that has only two *factors*: 1 and the number itself.	prime: 2, 3, 5, 7, 11, 13, 17…
product *(noun)*	The result of *multiplication*.	4 × 5 = ⃝20 product
property *(noun)*	A characteristic of a number, *operation*, or equality. (see *Additive Identity Property, Associative Property of Addition, Associative Property of Multiplication, Commutative Property of Addition, Commutative Property of Multiplication, Distributive Property, Inverse Property of Addition, Inverse Property of Multiplication, Multiplicative Identity Property*)	Distributive Property: 8 × 24 ∧ 8 × (20 + 4) (8 × 20) + (8 × 4) 160 + 32

MATH TERM	MEANING	EXAMPLE
proportion *(noun)*	An *equation* that compares two ratios. (see *ratio*)	$4 : 8 = 1 : 2$ $\frac{4}{8} = \frac{1}{2}$ 4 to 8 = 1 to 2
Q		
quantity *(noun)*	An amount that can be counted or measured; not a label.	There are ⃝54 students in Room ⃝54. quantity label
quotient *(noun)*	The result of *division*.	$24 \div 6 = ⃝4$ 6)⃝4̄̄ ⃝2̄4̄ quotient $\frac{24}{6} = ⃝4$ quotient quotient
R		
ratio *(noun)*	A *representation* comparing two quantities; specifically a part to a part of the same *whole*, a part to a whole, or a whole to a part. (see *proportion, quantity*)	$4 : 8$ $\frac{4}{8}$ 4 to 8
rational number *(noun)*	Numbers that can be expressed as the *quotient* of two *integers*, where the *divisor* does not *equal* zero. (see *repeating decimal number, integers, zero*)	rational number ⃝10 12 12)120 −6 −120 −3.56 0 $\frac{5}{4}$
reciprocal of a number *(noun)*	The number that you *multiply* another number by that gives a result of one. (see *inverse operation, multiplicative inverse*)	reciprocal of 6 $6 \times \left(\frac{1}{6}\right) = \frac{6}{6}$ or 1 $\frac{4}{3} \times \left(\frac{3}{4}\right) = \frac{12}{12}$ or 1 reciprocal of $\frac{4}{3}$
remainder *(noun)*	The *whole number* left over after *division*. (see *divisible*)	2 10 12 R3 6)75 −60 15 −12 ⃝3 remainder 75 ÷ 6 = 12 R3

MATH TERM	MEANING	EXAMPLE
repeating decimal number (noun)	A *decimal number* in which decimal digits repeat forever; generally shortened to a few repetitions of the repeating digits or represented with a line above the repeating digits. (see *digit*, *rational number*)	$\frac{1}{11} = 0.09090909...$ or $0.\overline{09}$ $\frac{1}{3} = 0.33333333...$ or $0.\overline{33}$
representation (noun)	The mathematical form used; different representations can reveal different information about a math problem. (see *model*, *symbolic form*)	representations of the number 1.6: 1 + 0.6 one and six-tenths
simplest form (adjective)	When the only *whole number* that divides both the *numerator* and *denominator* of a *fraction* evenly is 1. (see *divide*)	$\frac{2}{4} \div \frac{2}{2} = \left(\frac{1}{2}\right)$ simplest form
subtract (verb)	To take away one amount from another or to find the *difference* between two numbers. (see *subtraction*)	$9 - 7 = 2$
subtraction (noun)	The *operation* of finding the *difference* between two numbers. (see *subtract*)	$9 - 7 = 2$
sum (noun)	The result of *addition*.	$4 + 8 = \boxed{12}$ sum

MATH TERM	MEANING	EXAMPLE
symbol (noun)	A *representation* used to replace a word or phrase; symbols can be used to simplify a complex problem. (see *symbolic form*)	Common math symbols = is equal to > is greater than < is less than + plus − minus × times, multiplication ÷ division
symbolic form (noun)	A *representation* of a mathematical statement using symbols. (see *symbol*)	symbolic form: 5 + 3 = 8 word form: five plus three equals eight
ten-thousandths place (noun)	The fourth place to the right of the *decimal point*, which shows how many ten-thousandths are in a number; the digit's *value* in that place is the *digit* times $\frac{1}{10,000}$. (see *place value*)	2654.387⑨ ten-thousandths place
tens place (noun)	The second place to the left of the *decimal point*, which shows how many tens are in a number; the digit's *value* in that place is the *digit* times 10. (see *place value*)	26⑤4.3879 tens place
tenths place (noun)	The first place to the right of the *decimal point*, which shows how many tenths are in a number; the digit's *value* in that place is the *digit* times $\frac{1}{10}$. (see *place value*)	2654.③879 tenths place

MATH TERM	MEANING	EXAMPLE
thousands place (noun)	The fourth place to the left of the *decimal point*, which shows how many thousands are in a number; the digit's *value* in that place is the *digit* times 1000. (see *place value*)	2654.3879 thousands place
thousandths place (noun)	The third place to the right of the *decimal point*, which shows how many one-thousandths are in a number; the digit's *value* in that place is the *digit* times $\frac{1}{1000}$. (see *place value*)	2654.3879 thousandths place
unit fraction (noun)	One of the parts from an equally divided *whole*; its *numerator* is always 1. (see *divide*, *fraction*, *one-eighth*, *one-fourth*, *one-half*, *one-sixteenth*, *one-sixth*, *one-third*, *one-twelfth*)	$\frac{1}{4}$ unit fraction
unknown (noun)	The *value* you solve for in a problem. (see *algebra*, *variable*)	$4 \times 7 = \bigcirc$ unknown unknown $n + 8 = 12$ $\frac{3}{4} = \frac{\square}{8}$ unknown
value (noun)	A number or *quantity*; often used for the result of an *operation* or the solution for an *equation*; or the amount that a *digit* represents in a multi-digit number. (see *place value*)	The value of 5 in 2593 is 500.

MATH TERM	MEANING	EXAMPLE
variable (noun)	A *symbol* in an *expression* that represents a *value* that may change or be *unknown*. (see *algebra*)	$n + 8 = 12$ variable
Venn diagram (noun)	A visual *model* used to represent relationships between sets of numbers; sets are shown in either intersecting or non-intersecting circles; if intersecting, the intersection represents numbers that are members of all intersecting sets.	CIRCLE A Numbers divisible by 6 — 12 24 36 42 84 7 14 28 — CIRCLE B Numbers divisible by 7
volume (noun)	The measure of the amount of space inside a solid figure; volume is measured in cubic units; the *formula* for volume of a rectangular prism is $V = l \times w \times h$, where *l*, *w*, and *h* represent length, width, and height. (see *area*)	$V = l \times w \times h$
whole (noun)	The total amount; the size of a whole, along with the number of parts, determines the size of the parts. (see *fraction*)	1 whole $\frac{1}{2}$
whole number (noun)	The counting numbers and *zero*; {0, 1, 2, 3,…}.	0, 1, 2, 3,…
zero (noun)	A *whole number* that represents no size or *quantity*; an integer between –1 and 1 on a *number line*. (see *benchmark numbers*, *integers*)	–5 –4 –3 –2 –1 0 1 2 3 4 5 zero

CREDITS

LESSON 1

Block Preview

› **Think about the Anchor Video and answer this question.**

If you wanted to become an Olympic athlete, how would you prepare?

› **Explain your strategy.**

To become an Olympic athlete I would prepare by _____

_____

_____

LESSON 2

Brain Teaser

› **Solve this riddle.**

I am a decimal less than 1.

I have 4 times as many tenths as I do hundredths.

My number of hundredths is divisible by 2.

Which decimal am I? _____

› **How did you begin working on this riddle?**

I began working on this riddle by

_____

_____

LESSON 3

Tell Me All That You Can

› **About 0.43**

- _____
- _____
- _____
- _____

› **A student said, "You can write 0.43 as 43 hundreds or $\frac{43}{100}$."** **Do you agree with this student?**

I agree/disagree with this student

because _____

_____

Math in Technology

In this Block, you will explore how math is used in computers and technology.

CIVIL Engineers

built **30** new bridges and restored more than **13 miles** of waterways for the **2012** London Olympics.

BIOMEDICAL Engineers

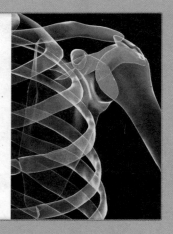

use technology to create devices, such as replacement knees and shoulders. This field is expected to grow **62%** by **2020**.

In many sporting events, a **hundredth of a second** can mean the difference between first and second place.

ATHLETIC Trainers

create training programs for student and pro athletes— and even for the military.

BROADCAST Technicians

operate the sound and video electronics for radio and television programs, including sporting events. They take special courses in vocational school to learn this trade.

Are you skilled with a video camera? About **25% of 27,000**

CAMERA Operators

in the United States work in television broadcasting, which includes TV shows, news, and live sporting events.